POEMS FROM FRANCE

POEMS FROM

FRANCE

Selected by William Jay Smith

Drawings by ROGER DUVOISIN

THOMAS Y. CROWELL COMPANY

NEW YORK

1 2 3 4 5 6 7 8 9 0

ACKNOWLEDGMENTS

The compiler of POEMS FROM FRANCE and the Thomas Y. Crowell Company wish to thank the following authors, translators, editors, publishers, and agents for permission to reprint copyrighted material. Every possible effort has been made to trace ownership of each poem and translation included. If any errors or omissions have occurred, and the publisher is notified of their existence, correction will be made in subsequent editions.

ATLANTIC–LITTLE, BROWN AND COMPANY for the translation by William Jay Smith of "Cathay" by Paul-Jean Toulet and the translation by William Jay Smith of "Les Grenades" ("Pomegranates") by Paul Valéry from *Poems 1947–1957* by William Jay Smith, copyright © 1957 by William Jay Smith. Reprinted by permission of Little, Brown and Company.

BOLLINGEN FOUNDATION for the two translations by Louise Varèse from *Éloges and Other Poems* by St.-John Perse, translated by Louise Varèse, Bollingen Series LV, copyright by Bollingen Foundation, New York, 1956, distributed by Pantheon Books, pp. 47, 49, reprinted by permission of Bollingen Foundation.

ANTHONY BOWER for his translation of Gérard de Nerval.

JONATHAN CAPE LTD. and WILLIAM PLOMER for translations of two epigrams by Voltaire: "Impromptu on Monsieur Turgot" and "To Monsieur Grétry" from *Collected Poems* by William Plomer. Reprinted by permission of Jonathan Cape Ltd.

CITY LIGHTS BOOKS for the translation by Lawrence Ferlinghetti of "Le Retour au Pays" ("The Homecoming") by Jacques Prévert, from *Selections from Paroles* by Jacques Prévert, copyright © 1947 by Les Editions du Point du Jour. Reprinted by permission of City Lights Books.

CHRISTOPHER CORNFORD and the EXECUTORS OF THE ESTATE OF FRANCES CORNFORD for the translation by Frances Cornford of José Maria de Heredia, which appeared originally in *Encounter*.

J. W. DENT LTD. and E. P. DUTTON & CO., INC., for the translations of "Épitaphe de Régnier" ("Epitaph on Himself") by Mathurin Régnier, and "Le Papillon" ("The Butterfly") by Alphonse de Lamartine, from the book *Chanticleer: A Study of the French Muse* by J. G. Legge, published by E. P. Dutton & Co., Inc., and reprinted by permission of the publishers.

POEMS OF THE WORLD
Under the editorship of Lillian Morrison

POEMS FROM FRANCE
Selected by William Jay Smith

POEMS FROM THE GERMAN
Selected by Helen Plotz

Table of Contents

Preface   1

POEMS   9

Biographies of the Poets   209

Index of Titles   219

Index of First Lines   221

Index of Poets   225

Index of Translators   226

TO SONJA

from her language to mine, with love

. . . Tout homme bien portant peut se passer de manger pendant deux jours,—de poésie jamais.

—CHARLES BAUDELAIRE
"Conseils aux jeunes littérateurs"

. . . Any man in good health can go without food for two days,—without poetry never.

—CHARLES BAUDELAIRE
"Advice to Young Writers"

Preface

There is surely no better testimony to the richness, variety, and vigor of French poetry through the centuries than the number of English poets of the first rank who have attempted to bring the best examples of it over into English. Eustache Deschamps, with whose poems this anthology opens, addressed one of his ballades to Chaucer, whom he called the "great translator." Many great poets since Chaucer have also been great translators: the English reader has only to look at Edmund Spenser's translations of Du Bellay to see how closely linked the poetic traditions of England and France once were. And he has only to examine the work of some of the finest poets, English and American, in the twentieth century, many of whose translations are gathered together here, to be aware of their debt to France. Jean Cocteau remarked that poetry, like electricity, is an old force which, as a force, was only recently discovered. The power of many great French poems will remain undiscovered by the English reader without great translators: poets, like electrical conductors, can channel poetic power from one language to another.

French poetry is, above all, vigorous and varied. Its heights may seem less startling at first than those of English poetry, largely because of the very great differences between the two languages. The development of French poetry is tied to the development of the language. French was until the seventeenth century a fluid and changing language which lent itself admirably to poetry. The lyrics of Ronsard and Du Bellay are natural and straight-forward in their diction: we hear in them, as we do in the sonnets

I

of Shakespeare, the voice of the poet, speaking to us in an easy conversational tone. In the seventeenth century the language underwent a purification and a codification totally unlike that of any other European country. It developed into a keen and sharp instrument capable of expressing ideas with great precision. But poetry, as Mallarmé was to remark much later, is made not with ideas but with words; and words in poetry require resonance more than precision. The purification of the language brought with it a rigid system of versification, with which French poets have had to deal, in one way or another, ever since.

A line of verse in English is governed by stress; in French it is based on syllabic count. There is properly speaking no metrical foot in French verse. The ten-syllable line was in Old French the usual meter of the French epic, and the eight-syllable line was also common in narrative, didactic, and dramatic poetry in the Middle Ages. The twelve-syllable line, the alexandrine, owes its name to the twelfth-century poem *Le Roman d'Alexandre*, describing the exploits of Alexander the Great, in which it was first prominently used. Ronsard and the poets of the Pléiade, a school of sixteenth-century poets whose aim it was to remodel the language, used it to advantage; in the seventeenth century it became the standard meter, used in all types of poetry down to the present. The alexandrine has its main pause, or *caesura*, after the sixth syllable, as in the opening line of the sonnet of Du Bellay:

> Heureux qui, comme Ulysse, a fait un beau voyage.

The difference between the French syllabic line and the English stressed one may be seen in the opening of La Fontaine's "Ode to Pleasure":

> O douce Volupté, sans qui, dès notre enfance,
> Le vivre et le mourir nous deviendraient égaux . . .

and the English translation of these lines by Richard Wilbur:

> Pleasure, whom had we lacked from earliest hour,
> To live or die had come to seem as one . . .

The accent of pitch in the French alexandrines, which forces the reader to give greater value to the vowels, has been transformed into a five-beat line in English. The subtle shift of vowels in the opening words, "*O douce Volupté*," where the sounds like musical notes convey the meaning to the ear, has had to be sacrificed in English although Mr. Wilbur has made an excellent attempt to keep something of the pleasure in sound that La Fontaine takes in writing about pleasure.

While offering a great variety of possibilities, the classical alexandrine at the same time imposed on poets severe restrictions. In the nineteenth century, Romantic poets like Victor Hugo tried to break out of the straitjacket which classical verse seemed to have become. Hugo shifted the caesura in the alexandrine, and made striking use of *enjambement* (run-over lines). (The classical alexandrine required a stop at the end of each line.) He also succeeded in reviving a variety of stanza forms. The breakup of the alexandrine was carried even further by Baudelaire and the poets who followed him. "Il faut tout casser," wrote Jules Laforgue late in the nineteenth century; and in order to break up everything, he proceeded to develop *vers libre* (free verse), liberated of all rules except that of musical cadence, permitting lines of uneven length and a free use of rhyme and assonance.

The rigidity of the French language has made French poetry far more rhetorical than that of other nations, and has given the poets of France the necessity of breaking down the formal restrictions to which they were heirs, or, as Paul Verlaine put it, of wringing the neck of rhetoric. The effort to do so has made French poets far more conscious artists than most of their English or American counterparts. English is so flexible a language, so multiple in its roots, that the poet absorbs almost unconsciously the demands of meter and rhyme; French, on the other hand, is so circumscribed that the poet must be first conscious of all the rules so that he may give himself fully to breaking them.

Eloquence is ingrained in the French nature. When asked to

lost to it. In compiling collections of translations, anthologists often do exactly the same thing. Their books become a dumping ground for all the wretched translations they can uncover, translations made by persons who know neither language adequately and who have no feeling for poetry. These horrors rest on library shelves year after year, and for those who are beginning to appreciate French poetry, they serve as a kind of obstacle course over which many will fail to triumph.

I have tried to give a sense of the immense variety of French poetry by selecting good poems and by discovering the best translations of them. My selection has naturally been limited by the translations available: many fine poems that I should have liked to include have still to find their translators. I have had to omit many great poems, such as "Le Cimetière Marin" of Paul Valéry, because their language, either in French or English, must remain outside the reach of those whose background of poetic reference and vocabulary is limited. The poems of Valéry that I have included are complex but accessible, on one level at least, on first reading; they will lead the reader on, I hope, to attempt for himself later the more difficult of his poems.

While trying to encompass the entire range of French poetry, I have had, because of restrictions of space, to make many sacrifices. I have included nothing of unknown authorship. France, especially during the period of the Middle Ages, is so rich in popular songs and ballads that an entire new collection by the best English translators should be made available. Neither have I touched the great field of narrative poetry; I have wished to give whole poems and not just excerpts.

This collection begins with poems written after the French language was more or less stabilized—with the great flowering of the Renaissance—and ends with poems of the present day. The translators range all the way from Edmund Spenser to Lawrence Ferlinghetti. Because of the great interest of English and American poets in French poetry since Baudelaire, I have given particular emphasis to the modern period. Many translations are by the greatest English and American poets, both past and present; others are the work of young poets who are only just beginning to publish. A number have never before appeared, having been made especially for this anthology. Not all of them are of the same level of merit by any means, but all, I trust, are competent, faithful, and readable. The translators have brought over into another medium, another language, another life. And by doing so, they have opened a new window on life for the English reader, allowing him to look out freshly at the world with that clarity that will remain forever one of France's greatest contributions.

WILLIAM JAY SMITH

POEMS

Eustache Deschamps

1346?–?1406

. .

VIRELAY

Sui je, sui je, sui je belle?

Il me semble, a mon avis,
Que j'ay beau front et doulz viz
Et la bouche vermeillette;
Dittes moy se je suis belle.

J'ay vers yeulx, petits sourcis,
Le chief blont, le nez traitis,
Ront menton, blanche gorgette;
Sui je, sui je, sui je belle?

J'ay dur sain et hault assis,
Lons bras, gresles doys aussis,
Et par le faulz sui greslette;
Dittes moy se je suis belle.

J'ay bonnes rains, ce m'est vis,
Bon dos, bon cul de Paris,
Cuisses et gambes bien faictes;
Sui je, sui je, sui je belle?

Eustache Deschamps

. .

VIRELAY

Am I lovely, am I fair?

In my opinion, I would say,
I've a sweet countenance, fresh face,
Vermillion-tinted are my lips;
Tell me, then, if I am fair.

Clear eyes have I, and eyebrows fine,
Hair that is blonde, a pleasing nose,
A rounded chin, a throat of white;
Am I lovely, am I fair?

Firm are my breasts, my carriage good,
Long arms and slender fingers too,
And so it follows that I'm deft;
Tell me, then, if I am fair.

I've proper hips, it seems to me,
Straight back, and elegant backside,
Thighs and legs well-made indeed;
Am I lovely, am I fair?

J'ay piez rondès et petiz,
Bien chaussans, et biaux habis,
Je sui gaye et foliette;
Dittes moy se je sui belle.

J'ay mantiaux fourrez de gris,
J'ay chapiaux, j'ay biaux proffis
Et d'argent mainte espinglette;
Sui je, sui je, sui je belle?

J'ay draps de soye et tabis,
J'ay draps d'or et blans et bis,
J'ay mainte bonne chosette;
Dittes moy se je sui belle.

Que .xv. ans n'ay, je vous dis;
Moult est mes tresors jolys,
S'en garderay la clavette;
Sui je, sui je, sui je belle?

Bien devra estre hardis
Cilz qui sera mes amis,
Qui ara tel damoiselle;
Dittes moy se je sui belle.

Et par Dieu je li plevis
Que tresloyal, se je vis,
Li seray, si ne chancelle;
Sui je, sui je, sui je belle?

Se courtois est et gentilz,
Vaillans, apers, bien apris,
Il gaignera sa querelle;
Dittes moy se je sui belle.

My feet are plump as well as small,
Well-shod and beautifully dressed
I am most gay and frolicsome;
Tell me, then, if I am fair.

Mantles fur-lined in grey have I,
Bonnets to spare, and money too,
And many a fancy silver pin;
Am I lovely, am I fair?

Robes of silk and taffeta,
Also of gold and white and beige,
I own many a pretty thing;
Tell me, then, if I am fair.

To say the truth: I'm but fifteen;
Various are these treasures sweet
Always a little key keeps safe;
Am I lovely, am I fair?

A man of daring must he be,
He who would become my lover,
Who such a maiden would possess;
Tell me, then, if I am fair.

And to him, by Our Lord, I'll swear
I shall be faithful, if I live,
And so remain, unless he waver;
Am I lovely, am I fair?

He who is courteous and kind,
Gallant, truly, and well formed,
He will surely win his race;
Tell me, then, if I am fair.

C'est un mondains paradiz
Que d'avoir dame toudis,
Ainsi fresche, ainsi nouvelle;
Sui je, sui je, sui je belle?

Entre vous accouardiz,
Pensez a ce que je diz;
Cy fine ma chansonelle;
Sui je, sui je, sui je belle?

An earthly paradise it would be
To have so many-virtued a lady,
So fresh as this, also so pleasing;
Am I lovely, am I fair?

Between your poor selves, then agree,
Considering what I have said;
And thus my little song is done;
Am I lovely, am I fair?

(*Barbara Howes*)

Christine de Pisan

1364–?1431

. .

CHRISTINE À SON FILS

Fils, je n'ai mie grand trésor
Pour t'enrichir, mais, au lieu d'or,
Aulcuns enseignements montrer
Te vueil, si les vueilles noter.

Dès ta jeunesse pure et monde,
Apprends à connaître le monde,
Si que tu puisses par apprendre
Garder en tous cas de méprendre.

Aie pitié des pauvres gens
Que tu vois nus et indigents,
Et leur aides quand tu pourras!
Souviengne toi que tu mourras.

Aime qui te tient ami
Et te gard' de ton ennemi:
Nul ne peut avoir trop d'amis,
Il est nuls petits ennemis.

Ne laisse pas que Dieu servir
Pour au monde trop asservir:
Car biens mondains vont à desfin
Et l'âme durera sans fin.

Christine de Pisan

.   .

CHRISTINE TO HER SON

SON, of great fortune have I none
To make you rich: instead of gold,
Though, certain lessons I would bring
Up, if you'll give them a hearing.

From first youth, innocent and pure,
Learn to know what people are,
And so, by seeing what they're like,
Protect yourself from gross mistake.

Upon the destitute take pity,
Poor creatures you will naked see,
Give them assistance as you may!
Bearing in mind you too will die.

Love him who is a friend to you
And watch out for your enemy:
No one can have too many friends,
There is no minor enemy.

What serves the Lord do not discard
For a world overmuch enslaved:
The worldly go to meet their fate
And the enduring soul holds out.

(*Barbara Howes*)

Charles d'Orléans
1391–1465

. .

RONDEAU

LE TEMPS a laissié son manteau
De vent, de froidure et de pluye,
Et s'est vestu de brouderie,
De soleil luyant, cler et beau.

Il n'y a beste, ne oyseau
Qu'en son jargon ne chante ou crie :
Le temps a laissié son manteau.
De vent, de froidure et de pluye.

Riviere, fontaine et ruisseau
Portent, en livree jolie,
Gouttes d'argent d'orfaverie ;
Chascun s'abille de nouveau :
Le temps a laissié son manteau.

BALLADE

EN LA FOREST de Longue Actente,
Chevauchant par divers sentiers
M'en voys, ceste annee presente,
Ou voyage de Desiriers.
Devant sont allez mes fourriers

Charles d'Orléans

. .

RONDEAU

THE YEAR has cast its cloak away
That was of driving rains and snows,
And now in flowered arras goes,
And wears the clear sun's glossy ray.

No bird or beast but seems to say
In cries or chipper tremolos:
The year has cast its cloak away
That was of driving rains and snows.

Stream, brook and silver fountain play,
And each upon itself bestows
A spangled livery as it flows;
All creatures are in fresh array:
The year has cast its cloak away.

(*Richard Wilbur*)

BALLADE—THE HOSTELRY OF THOUGHT

ACROSS the forest of Delay,
By many a winding woodland route,
This present year, full eagerly,
Drawn by desire have I set out.
The aides that I despatched have sought

Pour appareiller mon logeis
En la cité de Destinee;
Et pour mon cueur et moy ont pris
L'ostellerie de Pensee.

Je mayne des chevaulx quarente
Et autant pour mes officiers,
Voire, par Dieu, plus de soixante,
Sans les bagaiges et sommiers.
Loger nous fauldra par quartiers,
Se les hostelz sont trop petis;
Toutesfoiz, pour une vespree,
En gré prendray, soit mieulx ou pis,
L'ostellerie de Pensee.

Je despens chascun jour ma rente
En maintz travaulx avanturiers,
Dont est Fortune mal contente
Qui soutient contre moy Dangiers;
Mais Espoirs, s'ilz sont droicturiers
Et tiennent ce qu'ilz m'ont promis,
Je pense faire telle armée
Qu'auray, malgré mes ennemis,
L'ostellerie de Pensee.

Prince, vray Dieu de paradis,
Vostre grace me soit donnee,
Telle que treuve, a mon devis,
L'ostellerie de Pensee.

To find me lodging in the city
Of Destiny, and take what ought
To satisfy my heart and me,
The goodly hostelry of Thought.

And I have marshalled forty bay
Steeds, for my officers have brought
Sixty or more all told—pray
God!—and baggage-mules to boot.
If inns be wanting or all bought
Up, we will scatter readily;
Yet be it only for one night,
Whatever comes, I will essay
The goodly hostelry of Thought.

My ready funds I spend each day
In actions of some daring sort,
The which a jealous Fate who plays
Me cruelly takes in ill part.
But if my Hopes run high and straight,
And hold to what they promised me,
Such seasoned troops will I have wrought
I'll win, despite my enemy,
The goodly hostelry of Thought.

Prince, true heavenly deity,
Your grace I pray be my resort,
Until what I desire I see—
The goodly hostelry of Thought.

(Barbara Howes)

RONDEAU

Dieu, qu'il la fait bon regarder
La gracieuse, bonne et belle !
Pour les grans biens qui sont en elle,
Chascun est prest de la louer.

Qui se pourroit d'elle lasser ?
Tousjours sa beauté renouvelle.
Dieu, qu'i[l la fait bon regarder,]
La gra[cieuse, bonne et belle !]

Par deça ne dela la mer,
Ne sçay dame, ne damoiselle
Qui soit en tous biens parfais telle ;
C'est un songe que d'y penser.
Dieu, qu'i[l la fait bon regarder !]

DIEU QU'IL LA FAIT

God, that mad'st her well regard her,
How she is so fair and bonny;
For the great charms that are upon her
Ready are all folk to reward her.

Who could part him from her borders
When spells are always renewed on her?
God, that mad'st her well regard her,
How she is so fair and bonny.

From here to there to the sea's border,
Dame nor damsel there's not any
Hath of perfect charms so many.
Thoughts of her are of dream's order:
God, that mad'st her well regard her.

(*Ezra Pound*)

François Villon
1431–?1489

· ·

RONDEAU

Mort, j'appelle de ta rigueur,
Qui m'a ma maistresse ravie,
Et n'es pas encore assouvie,
Si tu ne me tiens en langueur.
Onc puis n'eus force ne vigueur;
Mais que te nuysoit elle en vie,
  Mort?
Deux estions et n'avions qu'ung cuer;
S'il est mort, force est que devie,
Voire, ou que je vive sans vie,
Comme les images, par cuer,
  Mort!

L'ÉPITAPHE VILLON (LA BALLADE DES PENDUS)

Freres humains qui après nous vivez,
N'ayez les cuers contre nous endurcis,
Car, se pitié de nous povres avez,
Dieu en aura plus tost de vous mercis.
Vous nous voyez ci attachés cinq, six;
Quant de la chair, que trop avons nourrie,
Elle est pieça devoree et pourrie,

François Villon

. .

TO DEATH, OF HIS LADY

DEATH, of thee do I make my moan,
  Who hadst my lady away from me,
  Nor wilt assuage thine enmity
Till with her life thou hast mine own;
For since that hour my strength has flown.
  Lo! what wrong was her life to thee,
        Death?

Two we were, and the heart was one;
  Which now being dead, dead I must be,
  Or seem alive as lifelessly
As in the choir the painted stone,
        Death!

                    (*Dante Gabriel Rossetti*)

BALLADE OF THE HANGED MEN

MEN and brothers, who after us shall be,
Let not your hearts too hard against us grow,
For if on us poor men you take pity,
God will be merciful to you also.
You see us, five or six, hung in a row,
That flesh we too much fattened long ago
Now tattered, eaten off, a rotten dough;

Et nous, les os, devenons cendre et poudre.
De nostre mal personne ne s'en rie,
Mais priez Dieu que tous nous veuille absoudre.

Se freres vous clamons, pas n'en devez
Avoir desdain, quoi que fusmes occis
Par justice. Toutesfois, vous savez
Que tous hommes n'ont pas bon sens rassis;
Excusez nous, puis que sommes transis,
Envers le fils de la Vierge Marie,
Que sa grace ne soit pour nous tarie,
Nous preservant de l'infernale foudre.
Nous sommes morts, ame ne nous harie;
Mais priez Dieu que tous nous veuille absoudre.

La pluie nous a debués et lavés,
Et le soleil dessechiés et noircis;
Pies, corbeaux, nous ont les yeux cavés,
Et arrachié la barbe et les sourcis.
Jamais nul temps nous ne sommes assis;
Puis ça, puis là, comme le vent varie,
A son plaisir sans cesser nous charie,
Plus becquetés d'oiseaux que dés à coudre.
Ne soiez donc de nostre confrerie;
Mais priez Dieu que tous nous veuille absoudre.

Prince Jesus, qui sur tous a maistrie,
Garde qu'Enfer n'ait de nous seigneurie;
A lui n'ayons que faire ne que soudre.
Hommes, ici n'a point de moquerie;
Mais priez Dieu que tous nous veuille absoudre.

And we, the bones, are growing pulverous.
Our wretchedness let no one laugh to see,
But pray God's mercy upon all of us.

If brother men you are, you need not be
Scornful of us, though Justice as I know
Cut short our lives. You know as well as we,
All men cannot be steady here below.
Forgive us, since we are transported so
To Mary's son, to kneel at his elbow,
And never may his fount of grace run low,
From thunderclap of Hell preserving us.
We are dead now, and mind no misery,
But pray God's mercy upon all of us.

The rain has drubbed us in his cold laundry,
The sun has parched us blacker than a crow,
And kites have made each eye a cavity
And torn out beards and eyebrows even so.
There is no resting place where we may go,
But here or there, just as the wind may blow,
We dangle at his pleasure to and fro,
Pocked more by birds than thimble surfaces.
Be not therefore of our fraternity,
But pray God's mercy upon all of us.

Prince Jesus, who hath all in mastery,
Over us let not Hell gain sovereignty,
For of it we are no way curious.
Brothers, see nothing here for mockery,
But pray God's mercy upon all of us.

(*Robert Fitzgerald*)

BALLADE DES DAMES DU TEMPS JADIS

DITES moi où, n'en quel pays
Est Flora la belle Romaine,
Archipiades, ne Thaïs,
Qui fut sa cousine germaine,
Echo, parlant quant bruit on maine
Dessus riviere ou sus estan,
Qui beauté eut trop plus qu'humaine.
Mais où sont les neiges d'antan?

Où est la tres sage Heloïs
Pour qui chastré fut et puis moine
Pierre Esbaillart à Saint Denis?
Pour son amour eut ceste essoine.
Semblablement, où est la roine
Qui commanda que Buridan
Fust jeté en un sac en Seine?
Mais où sont les neiges d'antan?

La roine Blanche comme lis
Qui chantoit à vois de seraine,
Berte au grant pié, Bietris, Alis,
Haremburgis qui tint le Maine,
Et Jehanne, la bonne Lorraine,
Qu'Anglois brulerent à Rouan;
Où sont ils, où, Vierge souvraine?...
Mais où sont les neiges d'antan!
Prince, n'enquerez de semaine
Où elles sont, ne de cest an,
Qu'à ce refrain ne vous remaine:
Mais où sont les neiges d'antan!

BALLADE OF THE LADIES OF TIME PAST

Oh TELL me where, in lands or seas,
Flora, that Roman belle, has strayed,
Thaïs, or Archipiades,
Who put each other in the shade,
Or Echo, who by bank and glade
Gave back the crying of the hound,
And whose sheer beauty could not fade.
But where shall last year's snow be found?

Where too is learned Heloise,
For whom shorn Abelard was made
A tonsured monk upon his knees?
Such tribute his devotion paid.
And where's that queen who, having played
With Buridan, had him bagged and bound
To swim the Seine thus ill-arrayed?
But where shall last year's snow be found?

Queen Blanche the fair, whose voice could please
As does the siren's serenade,
Big Bertha, Beatrice, Alice—these,
And Arembourg whom Maine obeyed,
And Joan whom Burgundy betrayed,
And England burned, and Heaven crowned:
Where are they, Mary, Sovereign Maid?
But where shall last year's snow be found?

Not next week, Prince, nor next decade,
Ask me these questions I propound.
I shall but say again, dismayed,
Ah, where shall last year's snow be found?

(*Richard Wilbur*)

Clément Marot

1496–1544

. .

DE SOY MESME

PLUS ne suis ce que j'ay esté,
Et ne le sçaurois jamais estre;
Mon beau printemps et mon esté
On fait le sault par la fenestre.
Amour, tu as esté mon maistre:
Je t'ai servi sur tous les dieux.
O si je pouvois deux fois naistre,
Comme je te servirois mieulx!

Clément Marot

. .

I AM NO MORE WHAT ONCE I WAS

I am no more what once I was,
And what I was, no more shall be;
My jolly summer and my spring
Have taken thieves' farewell of me.
O Love, how I have worshipped thee:
Above all gods I thee adore,
And were I twice-born I should be
But born again to serve thee more!

(*Katherine Anne Porter*)

Joachim du Bellay

1522–1560

. .

NOUVEAU VENU, QUI CHERCHES ROME EN ROME

NOUVEAU venu, qui cherches Rome en Rome,
Et rien de Rome en Rome n'apperçois,
Ces vieux palais, ces vieux arcz que tu vois,
Et ces vieux murs, c'est ce que Rome on nomme.

Voy quel orgueil, quelle ruine: et comme
Celle qui mist le monde sous ses loix,
Pour donter tout, se donta quelquefois,
Et devint proye au temps, qui tout consomme.

Rome de Rome est le seul monument,
Et Rome Rome a vaincu seulement.
Le Tybre seul, qui vers la mer s'enfuit,

Reste de Rome. O mondaine inconstance!
Ce qui est ferme, est par le temps destruit,
Et ce qui fuit, au temps fait resistance.

TOY QUI DE ROME

TOY qui de Rome emerueillé contemples
L'antique orgueil, qui menassoit les cieux,
Ces vieux palais, ces monts audacieux,
Ces murs, ces arcz, ces thermes, & ces temples,

Joachim du Bellay

. .

ROME

THOU stranger, which for *Rome* in *Rome* here seekest,
And nought of *Rome* in *Rome* perceiv'st at all,
These same olde walls, olde arches, which thou seest,
Olde Palaces, is that which *Rome* men call.
   Behold what wreake, what ruine, and what wast,
And how that she, which with her mightie power
Tam'd all the world, hath tam'd herselfe at last,
The prey of time, which all things doth devour.
   Rome now of *Rome* is th'onely funerall,
And onely *Rome* of *Rome* hath victorie;
Nor aught save Tyber hastning to his fall
Remaines of all: O world's inconstancie.
   That which is firme doth flit and fall away,
   And that is flitting, doth abide and stay.

(*Edmund Spenser*)

ROME

YOU, who behold in wonder Rome and all
   Her former passion, menacing the gods,
   These ancient palaces and baths, the sods
   Of seven hills, and temple, arch, and wall,

Iuge, en voyant ces ruines si amples,
  Ce qu'a ronge le temps iniurieux,
  Puis qu'aux ouuriers les plus industrieux
Regarde apres, comme de iour en iour
  Rome fouillant son antique seiour,
  Se rebatist de tant d'oeuures diuines:
Tu iugeras, que le daemon Romain
  S'efforce encor d'une fatale main
  Ressusciter ces poudreuses ruines.

HEUREUX QUI, COMME ULYSSE

Heureux qui, comme Ulysse, a fait un beau voyage,
Ou comme cestui-là qui conquit la toison,
Et puis est retourné, plein d'usage et raison,
Vivre entre ses parents le reste de son âge !

Quand reverrai-je, hélas, de mon petit village
Fumer la cheminée, et en quelle saison
Reverrai-je le clos de ma pauvre maison,
Qui m'est une province, et beaucoup d'avantage ?

Plus me plaît le séjour qu'ont bâti mes aïeux
Que des palais romains le front audacieux;
Plus que le marbre dur me plaît l'ardoise fine,

Plus mon Loire gaulois que le Tibre latin,
Plus mon petit Liré que le Mont Palatin,
Et plus que l'air marin la douceur angevine.

Consider, in the ruins of her fall,
    That which destroying Time has gnawed away—
    What workmen built with labor day by day
    Only a few worn fragments now recall.
Then look again and see where, endlessly
    Treading upon her own antiquity,
    Rome has rebuilt herself with works as just:
There you may see the demon of the land
    Forcing himself again with fatal hand
    To raise the city from this ruined dust.

(Yvor Winters)

HEUREUX QUI, COMME ULYSSE

GREAT joy be to the sailor if he chart
The Odyssey, or bear away the Fleece,
Yet unto wisdom's laurel and the peace
Of his own kind come lastly to his start.

And when shall I, being migrant, bring my heart
Home to its plots of parsley, its proper earth,
Pot hooks, cow dung, black chimney bricks whose worth
I have not skill to honor in my art.

I hold the colonnades of marble Rome
Nothing so perfect as my simple home:
Slate is my subtle stone, slate is my blue.

And bluer the Loire is to my reckoning
Than Caesar's Tiber, and more nourishing
Than salt spray is the breathing of Anjou.

(Anthony Hecht)

Pierre de Ronsard

1524–1585

· ·

QUAND VOUS SEREZ BIEN VIEILLE

QUAND vous serez bien vieille, au soir, à la chandelle,
Assise auprès du feu, devidant et filant,
Direz chantant mes vers, en vous esmerveillant:
Ronsard me celebroit du temps que j'estois belle.

Lors vous n'aurez servante oyant telle nouvelle,
Desja sous le labeur à demy sommeillant,
Qui au bruit de mon nom ne s'aille resveillant,
Benissant vostre nom de louange immortelle.

Je seray sous la terre, et, fantosme sans os,
Par les ombres myrteux je prendray mon repos:
Vous serez au fouyer une vieille accroupie,

Regrettant mon amour et vostre fier desdain.
Vivez, si m'en croyez, n'attendez à demain:
Cueillez dès aujourd'huy les roses de la vie.

Pierre de Ronsard

. .

WHEN YOU ARE OLD

WHEN you are old, at evening candle-lit
   beside the fire bending to your wool,
read out my verse and murmur, "Ronsard writ
   this praise for me when I was beautiful."
And not a maid but, at the sound of it,
   though nodding at the stitch on broidered stool,
will start awake, and bless love's benefit
   whose long fidelities bring Time to school.
I shall be thin and ghost beneath the earth
   by myrtle shade in quiet after pain,
but you, a crone, will crouch beside the hearth
   mourning my love and all your proud disdain.
And since what comes to-morrow who can say?
Live, pluck the roses of the world to-day.

(*Humbert Wolfe*)

COMME ON VOID SUR LA BRANCHE

COMME on void sur la branche au mois de May la rose,
En sa belle jeunesse, en sa premiere fleur,
Rendre le ciel jaloux de sa vive couleur,
Quand l'aube de ses pleurs au poinct du jour l'arrose:

La grace dans sa feuille, et l'amour se repose,
Embasmant les jardins et les arbres d'odeur:
Mais battue ou de pluye ou d'excessive ardeur,
Languissante elle meurt feuille à feuille déclose.

Ainsi en ta premiere et jeune nouveauté,
Quand la terre et le ciel honoroient ta beauté,
La Parque t'a tuée, et cendre tu reposes.

Pour obseques reçoy mes larmes et mes pleurs,
Ce vase plein de laict, ce pannier plein de fleurs,
Afin que vif et mort ton corps ne soit que roses.

ROSES

As ONE sees on the branch in the month of May the rose
In her beautiful youth, in the dawn of her flower,
When the break of day softens her life with the shower,
Make jealous the sky of the damask bloom she shows:
Grace lingers in her leaf and love sleeping glows
Enchanting with fragrance the trees of her bower,
But, broken by the rain or the sun's oppressive power,
Languishing she dies, and all her petals throws.
Thus in thy first youth, in thy awakening fair
When thy beauty was honored by lips of Earth and Air,
Atropos has killed thee and dust thy form reposes.
O take, take for obsequies my tears, these poor showers,
This vase filled with milk, this basket strewn with flowers,
That in death as in life thy body may be roses.

(Vernon Watkins)

Louise Labé

c. 1524–1566

· ·

SONNET VIII

IE VIS, ie meurs: ie me brule et me noye.
J'ay chaut estreme en endurant froidure:
La vie m'est et trop molle et trop dure.
J'ay grans ennuis entremeslez de ioye:

Tout à un coup ie ris et ie larmoye,
Et en plaisir maint grief tourment i'endure:
Mon bien s'en va, et à iamais il dure:
Tout en un coup ie seiche et ie verdoye.

Ainsi Amour inconstamment me meine:
Et quand ie pense auoir plus de douleur,
Sans y penser ie me treuue hors de peine.

Puis quand ie croy ma ioye estre certeine,
Et estre au haut de mon desiré heur,
Il me remet en mon premier malheur.

Louise Labé

. .

THE EIGHTH SONNET

I LIVE, I die. I drown, I am aflame.
I shake with cold and perish with the heat.
I leap from anguish to delight; from sweet
To bitter. No two moments are the same,

And all the leap of joy and lunge of gloom
Join in a single instant. Each delight
Aches with a hidden torment, and the night
Fades, yet survives. I wither, yet I bloom.

So Eros leads me on. And when at last
I know the full extremity of pain,
I feel, quite suddenly, at ease again,

Strangely at peace. And when once more I see
Some future hope, some present certainty,
He comes and flings the furies of the past!

(*Frederic Prokosch*)

Mathurin Régnier

1573–1613

· ·

ÉPITAPHE DE RÉGNIER

J'AY vécu sans nul pensement,
Me laissant aller doucement
A la bonne loy naturelle,
Et si m'étonne fort pourquoy
La mort osa songer à moy,
Qui ne songeay jamais à elle.

Mathurin Régnier

. .

EPITAPH ON HIMSELF

I'VE lived my life in careless ease,
And come and gone as best might please,
  Obeying nature's harmless call;
I wonder what the cause may be
That Death should turn her thoughts on me,
  Who never thought of her at all.

(*J. G. Legge*)

Jean de la Fontaine

1621–1695

. .

"O DOUCE VOLUPTÉ..."

O DOUCE Volupté, sans qui, dès notre enfance,
Le vivre et le mourir nous deviendraient égaux;
Aimant universel de tous les animaux,
Que tu sais attirer avecque violence!
 Par toi tout se meut ici-bas.
 C'est pour toi, c'est pour tes appas,
 Que nous courons après la peine:
 Il n'est soldat, ni capitaine,
Ni ministre d'Etat, ni prince, ni sujet,
 Qui ne t'ait pour unique objet.
Nous autres nourrissons, si pour fruit de nos veilles
Un bruit délicieux ne charmait nos oreilles,
Si nous ne nous sentions chatouillés de ce son,
 Ferions-nous un mot de chanson?
Ce qu'on appelle gloire en termes magnifiques,
Ce qui servait de prix dans les jeux olympiques,
N'est que toi proprement, divine Volupté.
Et le plaisir des sens n'est-il de rien compté?
 Pour quoi sont faits les dons de Flore,
 Le Soleil couchant et l'Aurore,
 Pomone et ses mets délicats,
 Bacchus, l'âme des bon repas,
 Les forêts, les eaux, les prairies,
 Mères des douces rêveries?
Pour quoi tant de beaux arts, qui tous sont tes enfants?
Mais pour quoi les Chloris aux appas triomphants,

Jean de la Fontaine

. .

ODE TO PLEASURE

PLEASURE, whom had we lacked from earliest hour,
To live or die had come to seem as one,
Of all creatures the sole magnet-stone,
How surely are we drawn by thy great power!
 Here, thou art mover of all things.
 For thee, for thy soft blandishings
 We fly to troubles and to harms.
 No captain is, nor man-at-arms,
Nor subject, minister, nor royalty,
 Who does not singly aim at thee.
We other nurslings, did not our labors bear
The fruits of fame, delicious to the ear,
And were this sound not pleasurably heard,
 Then should we rhyme a single word?
That which the world calls glory, and acclaims,
Which served as guerdon in the Olympic games,
Truly is none but thee, O divine Pleasure.
And shall the joys of sense not fill thy measure?
 For whom are Flora's gifts outlaid,
 The Sunset and Aurora made,
 Pomona and her tasty fare,
 Bacchus, soul of banquets rare,
 Waters, and forest-lands, and leas,
 The nourishers of reveries?
Wherefore so many arts, thy children all?
Why all these Chlorises, whose charms enthrall,

   Que pour maintenir ton commerce?
J'entends innocemment: sur son propre désir
   Quelque rigueur que l'on exerce,
   Encore y prend-on du plaisir.
Volupté, Volupté, qui fus jadis maîtresse
   Du plus bel esprit de la Grèce,
Ne me dédaigne pas, viens-t'en loger chez moi;
   Tu n'y seras pas sans emploi.
J'aime le jeu, l'amour, les livres, la musique,
La ville et la campagne, enfin tout; il n'est rien
   Qui ne me soit souverain bien,
Jusqu'au sombre plaisir d'un cœur mélancolique.
Viens donc; et de ce bien, ô douce Volupté,
Veux-tu savoir au vrai la mesure certaine?
Il m'en faut tout au moins un siècle bien compté;
   Car trente ans, ce n'est pas la peine.

LA CIGALE ET LA FOURMI

  La cigale, ayant chanté
   Tout l'été,
  Se trouva fort dépourvue
  Quand la bise fut venue:
  Pas un seul petit morceau
  De mouche ou de vermisseau.
  Elle alla crier famine
  Chez la fourmi sa voisine,
  La priant de lui prêter
  Quelque grain pour subsister
  Jusqu'à la saison nouvelle.

Unless to make thy commerce thrive?
My meaning's innocent: whatever limit
    Rigor may for desire contrive,
    Nevertheless there's pleasure in it.
O Pleasure, Pleasure, in the former age
    Mistress of Hellas' gayest sage,
Pray scorn me not, come thence and stop with me;
    Idle thou shalt never be:
For games I love, and love, and every art,
Country, and town, and all; there's nought my mood
    May not convert to sovereign good,
Even to the gloom of melancholy heart.
Then come; and wouldst thou know, O sweetest Pleasure,
What measure of these goods must me befall?
Enough to fill a hundred years of leisure;
    For thirty were no good at all.

(Richard Wilbur)

THE GRASSHOPPER AND THE ANT

GRASSHOPPER, having sung her song
    All summer long,
Was sadly unprovided-for
When the cold winds began to roar:
Not one least bite of grub or fly
Had she remembered to put by.
Therefore she hastened to descant
On famine, to her neighbor Ant,
Begging the loan of a few grains
Of wheat to ease her hunger-pains
Until the winter should be gone.

Je vous paierai, lui dit-elle,
Avant l'août, foi d'animal,
Intérêt et principal.
La fourmi n'est pas prêteuse :
C'est là son moindre défaut.
Que faisiez-vous au temps chaud ?
Dit-elle à cette emprunteuse. —
Nuit et jour à tout venant
Je chantais, ne vous déplaise. —
Vous chantiez ! j'en suis fort aise.
Eh bien ! dansez maintenant.

LE CHIEN QUI LÂCHE SA PROIE POUR L'OMBRE

CHACUN se trompe ici-bas :
On voit courir après l'ombre
Tant de fous qu'on n'en sait pas
La plupart du temps le nombre.
Au chien dont parle Ésope il faut les renvoyer.
Ce chien, voyant sa proie en l'eau représentée,
La quitta pour l'image, et pensa se noyer.
La rivière devint tout d'un coup agitée ;
A toute peine il regagna les bords,
Et n'eut ni l'ombre ni le corps.

"You shall be paid," said she, "upon
My honor as an animal,
Both interest and principal."
The Ant was not disposed to lend:
That liberal vice was not for her.
"What did you do all summer, friend?"
She asked the would-be borrower.
    "So please your worship," answered she,
"I sang and sang both night and day."
"You sang? Indeed, that pleases me.
Then dance the winter-time away."

(*Richard Wilbur*)

THE DOG WHO DROPPED SUBSTANCE FOR SHADOW

EVERYONE is self-deceived:
Of all the fooled, agog to catch a phantom,
The number if you knew it would never be believed;
It is a permanent conundrum.
We ought to be reminded of Aesop's dog, who set out
With a bone, but, on seeing what he had in his mouth doubled
By water, dropped it for the shadow and just about
Drowned. The brook was instantly troubled;
    And having worn himself out, he'd neither substance nor
        shadow to thank
    Himself for on regaining the bank.

(*Marianne Moore*)

François-Marie Arouet de Voltaire

1694–1778

. .

IMPROMPTU SUR M. TURGOT

JE CROIS en Turgot fermement:
Je ne sais pas ce qu'il veut faire,
Mais je sais que c'est le contraire
De ce qu'on fit jusqu'à présent.

A MONSIEUR GRÉTRY,

sur son opéra du *Jugement de Midas*, représenté sans succès
devant une nombreuse assemblée de grands seigneurs, et très-
applaudi quelques jours après sur le théâtre de Paris.

LA COUR a dénigré tes chants,
Dont Paris a dit des merveilles.
Hélas! les oreilles des grands
Sont souvent de grandes oreilles.

François-Marie Arouet de Voltaire

. .

IMPROMPTU ON MONSIEUR TURGOT

I FIRMLY believe in Turgot:
What he will do I don't know—
But I know it won't be, anyhow,
The same that's been done up to now.

TO MONSIEUR GRÉTRY

on his opera *The Judgment of Midas,* unsuccessfully played
before a full house of great lords, and very well received a
few days later at a theatre in Paris.

A TRIUMPH in Paris, your songs were decried
    At court, it appears:
Alas! often the ears of the mighty
    Are mighty long ears.

(*William Plomer*)

André Chénier

1762–1794

. .

LA FLÛTE

Toujours ce souvenir m'attendrit et me touche,
Quand lui-même, appliquant la flûte sur ma bouche,
Riant et m'asseyant sur lui, près de son coeur,
M'appelait son rival et déjà son vainqueur.
Il façonnait ma lèvre inhabile et peu sûre
A souffler une haleine harmonieuse et pure;
Et ses savantes mains prenaient mes jeunes doigts,
Les levaient, les baissaient, recommençaient vingt fois,
Leur enseignant ainsi, quoique faibles encore,
A fermer tour à tour les trous du buis sonore.

André Chénier

. .

THE FLUTE

I AM always touched by one memory of my youth—
How he himself, lifting the flute to my mouth,
Smiling as he took me on his knee, close to his heart,
Called me his rival, already master of his art.
He trained my lips, still clumsy and unsure,
To hold a note harmonious and pure;
He took my fingers in his knowing hands,
Raised them, then let them down, repeating his commands
Until, however weak they were, they understood
The stops that brought the music from the sounding wood.

(*Henry Taylor*)

Marceline Desbordes-Valmore

1786–1859

. .

LES ROSES DE SAADI

J'AI VOULU ce matin te rapporter des roses;
Mais j'en avais tant pris dans mes ceintures closes
Que les noeuds trop serrés n'ont pu les contenir.

Les noeuds ont éclaté. Les roses envolées
Dans le vent, à la mer s'en sont toutes allées;
Elles ont suivi l'eau pour ne plus revenir.

La vague en a paru rouge et comme enflammée:
Ce soir, ma robe encore en est tout embaumée...
Respires-en sur moi l'odorant souvenir.

Marceline Desbordes-Valmore

. .

THE ROSES OF SA'ADI

I WANTED this morning to bring you a gift of roses;
But I took so many in my wide belt,
The tightened knots could not contain them all,

And burst asunder. The roses taking wing
On the wind, were all blown out to sea,
Following the water, never to return;

The waves were red with them as if aflame.
This evening my dress bears their perfume still:
You may take from it now their fragrant souvenir.

(Barbara Howes)

Alphonse de Lamartine

1790–1869

. .

LE PAPILLON

NAÎTRE avec le printemps, mourir avec les roses;
Sur l'aile du zéphyr nager dans un ciel pur;
Balancé sur le sein des fleurs à peine écloses,
S'enivrer de parfums, de lumière et d'azur;
Secouant, jeune encor, la poudre de ses ailes,
S'envoler comme un souffle aux voûtes éternelles,
Voilà du papillon le destin enchanté.
Il ressemble au désir, qui jamais ne se pose,
Et sans se satisfaire, effleurant toute chose,
Retourne enfin au ciel chercher la volupté!

Alphonse de Lamartine

. .

THE BUTTERFLY

To COME to life with spring, and die when dies the rose;
Borne on a zephyr's wing to float in heaven's pure height;
Dandled upon a flower, whose petals scarce unclose,
To drug himself with scents and draughts of azure light;
And shaking from his wings, still young, the powdery down,
To flutter like a breath to earth's eternal crown;
Such is the butterfly's enchanted destiny.
How like Desire he is, that rests not in its flight,
But still unsatisfied, though kissing all things bright,
Returns at last to seek its pleasure in the sky!

(*J. G. Legge*)

Alfred de Vigny

1797–1863

. .

LA NATURE

ELLE me dit: "Je suis l'impassible théâtre
Que ne peut remuer le pied de ses acteurs;
Mes marches d'émeraude et mes parvis d'albâtre,
Mes colonnes de marbre ont les dieux pour sculpteurs.
Je n'entends ni vos cris ni vos soupirs; à peine
Je sens passer sur moi la comédie humaine
Qui cherche en vain au ciel ses muets spectateurs,

"Je roule avec dédain, sans voir et sans entendre,
A côté des fourmis les populations;
Je ne distingue pas leur terrier de leur cendre,
J'ignore en les portant les noms des nations.
On me dit une mère et je suis une tombe.
Mon hiver prend vos morts comme son hécatombe,
Mon printemps ne sent pas vos adorations.

"Avant vous, j'étais belle et toujours parfumée,
J'abandonnais au vent mes cheveux tout entiers,
Je suivais dans les cieux ma route accoutumée
Sur l'axe harmonieux des divins balanciers.
Après vous, traversant l'espace où tout s'élance,
J'irai seule et sereine, en un chaste silence
Je fendrai l'air du front et de mes seins altiers."

Alfred de Vigny

. .

NATURE

I AM the stage, impassive, mute and cold,
   That thrills not where the actor's foot hath trod.
My alabaster halls, my emerald
   Stairs, and my tones were sculptured by a god:
Your voice of crying I know not, no, nor see
The passing of the human comedy
   That looks to heaven to find its period.
I roll, and to my deep disdain I thrust
   The seed of ants and human populations;
Their tenements I know not from their dust,
   Their names I know not—I that bear the nations;
Mother in name, in deed a very room
For death; my winter takes its hecatomb,
   My spring is careless of your adorations.

Before you, always essenced, always fair,
   I shook my locks abroad the winds of heaven,
And trod my customary path in air,
   While the divine hands held the balance even:
And onward, to that void where all things roll
I shall be carried silently and sole,
   And by my breast and brows the airs be riven.

(*Margaret Jourdain*)

Victor Hugo

1802–1885

. .

SOLEILS COUCHANTS

Merveilleux tableaux que la vue découvre à la pensée.
—CHARLES NODIER

J'AIME les soirs sereins et beaux, j'aime les soirs,
Soit qu'ils dorent le front des antiques manoirs
    Ensevelis dans les feuillages;
Soit que la brume au loin s'allonge en bancs de feu;
Soit que mille rayons brisent dans un ciel bleu
    A des archipels de nuages.

Oh! regardez le ciel! cent nuages mouvants,
Amoncelés là-haut sous le souffle des vents,
    Groupent leurs formes inconnues;
Sous leurs flots par moments flamboie un pâle éclair,
Comme si tout à coup quelque géant de l'air
    Tirait son glaive dans les nues.

Le soleil, à travers leurs ombres, brille encor;
Tantôt fait, à l'égal des larges dômes d'or,
    Luire le toit d'une chaumière;
Ou dispute aux brouillards les vagues horizons;
Ou découpe, en tombant sur les sombres gazons,
    Comme de grands lacs de lumière.

Puis voilà qu'on croit voir, dans le ciel balayé,
Pendre un grand crocodile au dos large et rayé,
    Aux trois rangs de dents acérées;

Victor Hugo

. .

A SUNSET

I LOVE the evenings, passionless and fair, I love the evens,
Whether old manor-fronts their ray with golden fulgence leavens,
  In numerous leafage bosomed close;
Whether the mist in reefs of fire extend its reaches sheer,
Or a hundred sunbeams splinter in an azure atmosphere
  On cloudy archipelagos.

Oh, gaze ye on the firmament! a hundred clouds in motion,
Up-piled in the immense sublime beneath the winds' commotion,
  Their unimagined shapes accord:
Under their waves at intervals flame a pale levin through,
As if some giant of the air amid the vapors drew
  A sudden elemental sword.

The sun at bay with splendid thrusts still keeps the sullen fold;
And momently at distance sets, as a cupola of gold,
  The thatched roof of a cot a-glance;
Or on the blurred horizon joins his battle with the haze;
Or pools the glooming fields about with inter-isolate blaze,
  Great moveless meres of radiance.

Then mark you how there hangs athwart the firmament's swept
    track,
Yonder, a mighty crocodile with vast irradiant back,
  A triple row of pointed teeth?

Sous son ventre plombé glisse un rayon du soir ;
Cent nuages ardents luisent sous son flanc noir
  Comme des écailles dorées.

Puis se dresse un palais. Puis l'air tremble, et tout fuit.
L'édifice effrayant des nuages détruit
  S'écroule en ruines pressées ;
Il jonche au loin le ciel, et ses cônes vermeils
Pendent, la pointe en bas, sur nos têtes, pareils
  A des montagnes renversées.

Ces nuages de plomb, d'or, de cuivre, de fer,
Où l'ouragan, la trombe, et la foudre, et l'enfer
  Dorment avec de sourds murmures,
C'est Dieu qui les suspend en foule aux cieux profonds,
Comme un guerrier qui pend aux poutres des plafonds
  Ses retentissantes armures.

Tout s'en va ! Le soleil, d'en haut précipité,
Comme un globe d'airain qui, rouge, est rejeté
  Dans les fournaises remuées,
En tombant sur leurs flots que son choc désunit
Fait en flocons de feu jaillir jusqu'au zénith
  L'ardente écume des nuées.

Oh ! contemplez le ciel ! et dès qu'a fui le jour,
En tout temps, en tout lieu, d'un ineffable amour,
  Regardez à travers ses voiles ;
Un mystère est au fond de leur grave beauté,
L'hiver, quand ils sont noirs comme un linceul, l'été,
  Quand la nuit les brode d'étoiles.

Under its burnished belly slips a ray of eventide,
The flickerings of a hundred glowing clouds its tenebrous side
   With scales of golden mail ensheathe.

Then mounts a palace, then the air vibrates—the vision flees.
Confounded to its base, the fearful cloudy edifice
   Ruins immense in mounded wrack;
Afar the fragments strew the sky, and each envermeiled cone
Hangeth, peak downward, overhead, like mountains overthrown
   When the earthquake heaves its hugy back.

These vapors, with their leaden, golden, iron, bronzèd glows,
Where the hurricane, the waterspout, thunder, and hell repose,
   Muttering hoarse dreams of destined harms,—
'Tis God who hangs their multitude amid the skiey deep,
As a warrior that suspendeth from the roof-tree of his keep
   His dreadful and resounding arms!

All vanishes! The Sun, from topmost heaven precipitated,
Like a globe of iron which is tossed back fiery red
   Into the furnace stirred to fume,
Shocking the cloudy surges, plashed from its impetuous ire,
Even to the zenith spattereth in a flecking scud of fire
   The vaporous and inflamèd spume.

O contemplate the heavens! Whenas the vein-drawn day dies pale,
In every season, every place, gaze through their every veil?
   With love that has not speech for need!
Beneath their solemn beauty is a mystery infinite:
If winter hue them like a pall, or if the summer night
   Fantasy them starry brede.

(Francis Thompson)

LES ENFANTS PAUVRES

PRENEZ garde à ce petit être;
Il est bien grand, il contient Dieu.
Les enfants sont, avant de naître,
Des lumières dans le ciel bleu.

Dieu nous les offre en sa largesse;
Ils viennent; Dieu nous en fait don;
Dans leur rire il met sa sagesse
Et dans leur baiser son pardon.

Leur douce clarté nous effleure.
Hélas, le bonheur est leur droit.
S'ils ont faim, le paradis pleure,
Et le ciel tremble, s'ils ont froid.

La misère de l'innocence
Accuse l'homme vicieux.
L'homme tient l'ange en sa puissance.
Oh! quel tonnerre au fond des cieux,

Quand Dieu, cherchant ces êtres frêles
Que dans l'ombre où nous sommeillons
Il nous envoie avec des ailes,
Les retrouve avec des haillons!

LA MÉRIDIENNE DU LION

LE LION dort, seul sous sa voûte.
Il dort de ce puissant sommeil
De la sieste, auquel s'ajoute,
Comme un poids sombre, le soleil.

THE CHILDREN OF THE POOR

TAKE heed of this small child of earth;
   He is great: he hath in him God most high.
Children before their fleshly birth
   Are lights alive in the blue sky.

In our light bitter world of wrong
   They come; God gives us them awhile.
His speech is in their stammering tongue,
   And his forgiveness in their smile.

Their sweet light rests upon our eyes.
   Alas! their right to joy is plain.
If they are hungry, Paradise
   Weeps, and, if cold, Heaven thrills with pain.

The want that saps their sinless flower
   Speaks judgment on sin's ministers.
Man holds an angel in his power.
   Ah! deep in Heaven what thunder stirs,

When God seeks out these tender things
   Whom in the shadow where we sleep
He sends us clothed about with wings,
   And finds them ragged babes that weep!

                (*Algernon Charles Swinburne*)

THE LION AT NOON

IN HIS lone cave the lion sleeps
   That powerful noonday sleep
To which the sun gives added weight,
   Making it still more deep.

Les déserts, qui de loin écoutent,
Respirent; le maître est rentré.
Car les solitudes redoutent
Ce promeneur démesuré.

Son souffle soulève son ventre;
Son œil de brume est submergé,
Il dort sur le pavé de l'antre,
Formidablement allongé.

La paix est sur son grand visage,
Et l'oubli même, car il dort.
Il a l'altier sourcil du sage
Et l'ongle tranquille du fort.

Midi sèche l'eau des citernes;
Rien du sommeil ne le distrait;
Sa gueule ressemble aux cavernes,
Et sa crinière à la forêt.

Il entrevoit des monts difformes,
Des Ossas et des Pélions,
À travers les songes énormes
Que peuvent faire les lions.

Tout se tait sur la roche plate
Où ses pas tout à l'heure erraient.
S'il remuait sa grosse patte,
Que de mouches s'envoleraient!

The deserts, listening from far,
　Breathe, for their lord has gone;
All solitary places fear
　This boundless wandering one.

His great chest heaves with every breath,
　Mist covers both his eyes;
On the den's floor, in heavy sleep,
　Stretched at full length he lies.

His mighty countenance displays
　Peace and oblivion now.
He has the conqueror's quiet claw,
　The sage's haughty brow.

Mid-day has dried the water-pools,
　Distractions all are vain:
How like a cavern his vast mouth!
　A forest is his mane!

Ossas and Pelions loom up,
　Strange mountain-summits show,
In those obscure enormous dreams
　That only lions know.

Upon the flat rock where his steps
　Fell lately, silence lies:
If he should move his massive paw,
　Lo, what a cloud of flies!

(*Eva Martin*)

SAISON DES SEMAILLES. LE SOIR

C'est le moment crépusculaire.
J'admire, assis sous un portail,
Ce reste de jour dont s'éclaire
La dernière heure du travail.

Dans les terres, de nuit baignées,
Je contemple, ému, les haillons
D'un vieillard qui jette à poignées
La moisson future aux sillons.

Sa haute silhouette noire
Domine les profonds labours.
On sent à quel point il doit croire
A la fuite utile des jours.

Il marche dans la plaine immense,
Va, vient, lance la graine au loin,
Rouvre sa main, et recommence,
Et je médite, obscur témoin,

Pendant que, déployant ses voiles,
L'ombre, où se mêle une rumeur,
Semble élargir jusqu'aux étoiles
Le geste auguste du semeur.

SOWING AT EVENING

Now is the moment of twilight.
I wonder, seated by this portal,
At the remaining day which lights
Up the final hour of toil.

There in the field, awash with night,
I watch, moved, as an old fellow,
In tatters, by the handful casts
The future harvest to the furrows.

How tall his darkened silhouette
Looms above this well-ploughed way;
One feels how deeply he must credit
The useful passage of each day.

He strides across the giant plain,
Back and forth, flings far the seed,
Opens his hand, begins again,
And I, a hidden witness, heed

While, its veils unfolding far,
Darkness—with its muffled roar—
Seems to heighten to the stars
The noble gesture of the sower.

(*Barbara Howes*)

Gérard de Nerval

1808–1855

. .

EL DESDICHADO

Je suis le ténébreux,—le veuf,—l'inconsolé,
Le prince d'Aquitaine à la tour abolie:
Ma seule *étoile* est morte—et mon luth constellé
Porte le *soleil noir* de la *Mélancolie*.

Dans la nuit du tombeau, toi qui m'as consolé,
Rends-moi le Pausilippe et la mer d'Italie,
La *fleur* qui plaisait tant à mon coeur désolé
Et la treille où le pampre à la rose s'allie.

Suis-je Amour ou Phébus, Lusignan ou Biron?
Mon front est rouge encor du baiser de la reine;
J'ai rêvé dans la grotte où nage la sirène…

Et j'ai deux fois vainqueur traversé l'Achéron:
Modulant tour à tour sur la lyre d'Orphée
Le soupirs de la sainte et les cris de la fée.

FANTAISIE

Il est un air pour qui je donnerais
Tout Rossini, tout Mozart et tout Weber
Un air très vieux, languissant et funèbre,
Qui pour moi seul a des charmes secrets.

Or, chaque fois que je viens à l'entendre,
De deux cents ans mon âme rajeunit:

Gérard de Nerval

• •

EL DESDICHADO

THE dark one am I, the widowed, unconsoled,
Prince of Aquitania whose tower lies ruined,
My one star is dead, and my radiant lute
Renders only the black sun of Melancholy.

In the night of the tomb, oh, you, my consoler,
Give me back Posilipo and the Italian sea,
The flower which delighted my desolate heart,
And the trellis where the vine and the roses marry.

Am I Eros or Phoebus, Lusignan or Biron?
My brow is still red with the kiss of the Queen;
I have dreamed in the grotto where the siren swims . . .

And twice have I, victor, crossed the Acheron:
Passing, in turn, on Orpheus' lyre
From the sighs of a saint to a fairy's cries.

(Barbara Howes)

FANTASY

THERE is an air for which I'd gladly give
All Mozart, all Rossini, all von Weber,
A languid, ancient, solemn-sounding air
That yields its secret charm to me alone.

Each time it happens that I hear it played
My heart grows younger by two hundred years:

C'est sous Louis-Treize...—Et je crois voir s'étendre
Un coteau vert que le couchant jaunit;

Puis un château de brique à coins de pierre,
Aux vitraux teints de rougeâtres couleurs,
Ceint de grands parcs, avec une rivière
Baignant ses pieds, qui coule entre des fleurs.

Puis une dame, à sa haute fenêtre,
Blonde aux yeux noirs, en ses habits anciens...
Que, dans une autre existence peut-être,
J'ai déjà vue—et dont je me souviens!

ÉPITAPHE

IL A vécu, tantôt gai comme un sansonnet,
Tour à tour amoureux, insoucieux et tendre,
Tantôt sombre et rêveur, comme un triste Clitandre.
Un jour, il entendit qu'à sa porte on sonnait:

C'était la mort. Alors, il la pria d'attendre
Qu'il eût posé le point à son dernier sonnet;
Et puis, sans s'émouvoir, il s'en alla s'étendre
Au fond du coffre froid où son corps frissonnait.

It était paresseux, à ce que dit l'histoire;
Il laissait trop sécher l'encre dans l'écritoire;
Il voulut tout savoir, mais il n'a rien connu;

Et quand vint le moment où, las de cette vie,
Un soir d'hiver, enfin, l'âme lui fut ravie,
Il s'en alla, disant: "Pourquoi suis-je venu?"

I live in former times . . . and see portrayed
A green slope gilded by the setting sun,

And then a feudal castle flanked with stone,
Its windows tinted to a glowing rose,
Bounded by spacious parks and with its feet
Bathed by a stream that through a garden flows.

And then a lady in a window high,
Fair-haired, dark-eyed and dressed in ancient style
Whom, in another life, perhaps I've seen,
And whom I now remember with a sigh.

(Anthony Bower)

EPITAPH

Now, like a starling's, all his life was gay—
Amorous, careless, tender—each in turn;
Now, a sad lover, dreamy . . . taciturn . . .
He heard a knocking at his door one day,

And it was Death! He asked his guest to stay
While his last sonnet found its final line,
Then calmly he arranged his body in
His icy coffin; shivering there he lay.

He was too lazy (so the tales implied);
Too often in his desk his ink-well dried.
All things he longed to know—but nothing knew.

And when he found his joy in life grow dim,
One winter night his soul was snatched from him . . .
"Why did I come?" he asked—and so withdrew.

(Brian Hill)

Alfred de Musset

1810–1857

. .

TRISTESSE

J'AI PERDU ma force et ma vie,
Et mes amis et ma gaieté;
J'ai perdu jusqu'à la fierté
Qui faisait croire à mon génie.

Quand j'ai connu la Vérité,
J'ai cru que c'était une amie;
Quand je l'ai comprise et sentie,
J'en étais déjà dégoûté.

Et pourtant elle est éternelle,
Et ceux qui se sont passés d'elle
Ici-bas ont tout ignoré.

Dieu parle, il faut qu'on lui réponde;
Le seul bien qui me reste au monde
Est d'avoir quelquefois pleuré.

Alfred de Musset

. .

SORROW

I'VE LOST my spirit and my strength,
My friends and my vitality;
Even that pride I've lost nearly
Which in my genius gave me faith.

When first I came to Truth, I thought
She'd be a friend to me, but when
I understood her well, by then
I was disgusted and worn out.

Although she is immortal, yet
Those who have done without her know
Nothing about life here below.

God speaks, and one must make reply;
The sole good that is left to me
In this world is having sometimes wept.

(*Barbara Howes*)

Théophile Gautier

1811–1872

. .

L'ART

Oui, l'œuvre sort plus belle
D'une forme au travail
   Rebelle,
Vers, marbre, onyx, émail.

Point de contraintes fausses !
Mais que pour marcher droit
   Tu chausses,
Muse, un cothurne étroit.

Fi du rhythme commode,
Comme un soulier trop grand,
   Du mode
Que tout pied quitte et prend !

Statuaire, repousse
L'argile que pétrit
   Le pouce
Quand flotte ailleurs l'esprit.

Lutte avec le carrare,
Avec le paros dur
   Et rare,
Gardiens du contour pur,

Théophile Gautier

· ·

ART

ALL things are doubly fair
If patience fashion them
    And care—
Verse, enamel, marble, gem.

No idle chains endure:
Yet, Muse, to walk aright
    Lace tight
Thy buskin proud and sure.

Fie on facile measure,
A shoe where every lout
    At pleasure
Slip his foot in and out!

Sculptor lay by the clay
On which thy nerveless finger
    May linger,
Thy thoughts flown far away.

Keep to Carrara rare,
Struggle with Paros cold,
    That hold
The subtle line and fair.

Emprunte à Syracuse
Son bronze où fermement
    S'accuse
Le trait fier et charmant;

D'une main délicate
Poursuis dans un filon
    D'agate
Le profil d'Apollon.

Lest haply nature lose
That proud, that perfect line,
    Make thine
The bronze of Syracuse.

And with a tender dread
Upon an agate's face
    Retrace
Apollo's golden head.

Peintre, fuis l'aquarelle,
Et fixe la couleur
   Trop frêle
Au four de l'émailleur.

Fais les sirènes bleues,
Tordant de cent façons
   Leurs queues,
Les monstres des blasons;

Dans son nimbe trilobe
La Vierge et son Jésus,
   Le globe
Avec la croix dessus.

Tout passe.—L'art robuste
Seul a l'éternité,
   Le buste
Survit à la cité,

Et la médaille austère
Que trouve un laboureur
   Sous terre
Révèle un empereur.

Les dieux eux-mêmes meurent,
Mais les vers souverains
   Demeurent
Plus fort que les airains.

Sculpte, lime, cisèle;
Que ton rêve flottant
   Se scelle
Dans le bloc résistant!

Despise a watery hue
And tints that soon expire.
    With fire
Burn thine enamel true.

Twine, twine in artful wise
The blue-green mermaid's arms,
    Mid charms
Of thousand heraldries.

Show in their triple lobe
Virgin and Child, that hold
    Their globe,
Cross crowned and aureoled.

—All things return to dust
Save beauties fashioned well;
    The bust
Outlasts the citadel.

Oft doth the plowman's heel,
Breaking an ancient clod,
    Reveal
A Cæsar or a god.

The gods, too, die, alas!
But deathless and more strong
    Than brass
Remains the sovereign song.

Chisel and carve and file,
Till thy vague dream imprint
    Its smile
On the unyielding flint.

(George Santayana)

LE POT DE FLEURS

PARFOIS un enfant trouve une petite graine,
Et tout d'abord, charmé des ses vives couleurs,
Pour la planter, il prend un pot de porcelaine
Orné de dragons bleus et de bizarres fleurs.

Il s'en va. La racine en couleuvres s'allonge,
Sort de terre, fleurit et devient arbrisseau;
Chaque jour, plus avant son pied chevelu plonge
Tant qu'il fasse éclater le ventre du vaisseau.

L'enfant revient; surpris, il voit la plante grasse
Sur les débris du pot brandir ses verts poignards;
Il la veut arracher, mais sa tige est tenace;
Il s'obstine, et ses doigt s'ensanglantent aux dards.

Ainsi germa l'amour dans mon âme surprise:
Je croyais ne semer qu'une fleur de printemps;
C'est un grand aloès dont la racine brise
Le pot de porcelaine aux dessins éclatants.

CHINOISERIE

CE N'EST pas vous, non, madame, que j'aime,
Ni vous non plus, Juliette, ni vous,
Ophélia, ni Béatrix, ni même
Laure la blonde, avec ses grands yeux doux.

Celle que j'aime, à présent, est en Chine;
Elle demeure avec ses vieux parents,
Dans une tour de porcelaine fine,
Au fleuve Jaune, où sont les cormorans.

THE POT OF FLOWERS

SOMETIMES a small boy finds a tiny seed
And takes a porcelain pot whose colours charm
His eye to serve it as a garden-bed,
Where monstrous blossoms and blue dragons swarm.

He goes away. Down snakes the coiling root;
The stem lifts from the soil, grows, branches out;
While deeper daily dives its hairy foot,
Until it bursts the belly of the pot.

The child comes back. He wonders much to see
Above the shards the stout green daggers dart;
The stalk is tough; he cannot tug it free;
Against the thorns his stubborn fingers smart.

So, in my wondering soul, is love begot:
A simple flower of Spring I thought I'd sown;
In coloured fragments lies the porcelain pot
Where a huge aloe's root went thrusting down!

(Brian Hill)

CHINOISERIE

IT IS not you, no, madam, whom I love,
Nor you either, Juliet, nor you,
Ophelia, nor Beatrice, nor that dove,
Fair-haired Laura with the big eyes; No.

She is in China whom I love just now;
She lives at home and cares for her old parents;
From a tower of porcelain she leans her brow,
By the Yellow River, where haunt the cormorants.

Elle a des yeux retroussés vers les tempes,
Un pied petit à tenir dans la main,
Le teint plus clair que le cuivre des lampes,
Les ongles longs et rougis de carmin.

Par son treillis elle passe sa tête,
Que l'hirondelle, en volant, vient toucher;
Et, chaque soir, aussi bien qu'un poète,
Chante le saule et la fleur du pêcher.

L'HIPPOPOTAME

L'HIPPOPOTAME au large ventre
Habite aux jungles de Java,
Où grondent, au fond de chaque antre,
Plus de monstres qu'on n'en rêva.

Le boa se déroule et siffle,
Le tigre fait son hurlement,
Le buffle en colère renifle,
Lui dort ou paît tranquillement.

Il ne craint ni kriss ni zagaies,
Il regarde l'homme sans fuir,
Et rit des balles des cipayes
Qui rebondissent sur son cuir.

Je suis comme l'hippopotame:
De ma conviction couvert,
Forte armure que rien n'entame,
Je vais sans peur par le désert.

She has upward-slanting eyes, a foot to hold
In your hand—that small; the colour shed
By lamps is less clear than her coppery gold;
And her long nails are stained with carmine red.

From her trellis she leans out so far
That the dipping swallows are within her reach,
And like a poet, to the evening star
She sings the willow and the flowering peach.

(*A. J. M. Smith*)

THE HIPPOPOTAMUS

THE HIPPO, huge of abdomen,
In darkest Java's jungle dwells,
Where from the depths of every den
More monsters snarl than dream can tell.

The boa comes uncoiled and hisses,
The tiger launches forth his roar,
The angry water buffalo sneezes,—
Quiet, he rests, or pastures, for

He fears nor kriss nor javelin,
He looks at man and never hides,
Unruffled, notes the Indian
Bullets rebounding from his sides.

A hippopotamus I am;
My basic certainty is this:
As nothing hurts the strongly armed,
Whole deserts can I range with ease.

(*Barbara Howes*)

Leconte de Lisle

1818–1894

. .

LE CŒUR DE HIALMAR

Une nuit claire, un vent glacé. La neige est rouge.
Mille braves sont là qui dorment sans tombeaux,
L'épée au poing, les yeux hagards. Pas un ne bouge.
Au-dessus tourne et crie un vol de noirs corbeaux.

La lune froide verse au loin sa pâle flamme.
Hialmar se soulève entre les morts sanglants,
Appuyé des deux mains au tronçon de sa lame.
La pourpre du combat ruisselle de ses flancs.

—Holà! Quelqu'un a-t-il encore un peu d'haleine,
Parmi tant de joyeux et robustes garçons
Qui, ce matin, riaient et chantaient à voix pleine
Comme des merles dans l'épaisseur des buissons?

Tous sont muets. Mon casque est rompu, mon armure
Est trouée, et la hache a fait sauter ses clous.
Mes yeux saignent. J'entends un immense murmure
Pareil aux hurlements de la mer ou des loups.

Viens par ici, Corbeau, mon brave mangeur d'hommes
Ouvre-moi la poitrine avec ton bec de fer.
Tu nous retrouveras demain tels que nous sommes.
Porte mon cœur tout chaud à la fille d'Ylmer.

Leconte de Lisle

. .

HIALMAR SPEAKS TO THE RAVEN

NIGHT in the bloodstained snow: the wind is chill:
And there a thousand tombless warriors lie,
Grasping their swords, wild-featured. All are still.
Above them the black ravens wheel and cry.

A brilliant moon sends her cold light abroad:
Hialmar arises from the reddened slain,
Heavily leaning on his broken sword, ·
And bleeding from his side the battle-rain.

"Hail to you all: is there one breath still drawn
Among those fierce and fearless lads who played
So merrily, and sang as sweet in the dawn
As thrushes singing in the bramble shade?

"They have no word to say: my helm's unbound,
My breastplate by the ax unriveted:
Blood's on my eyes; I hear a spreading sound,
Like waves or wolves that clamor in my head.

"Eater of men, old raven, come this way,
And with thine iron bill open my breast,
To-morrow find us where we lie to-day,
And bear my heart to her that I love best.

Dans Upsal, où les Jarls boivent la bonne bière,
Et chantent, en heurtant les cruches d'or, en chœur,
A tire-d'aile vole, ô rôdeur de bruyère !
Cherche ma fiancée et porte lui mon cœur.

Au sommet de la tour que hantent les corneilles
Tu la verras debout, blanche, aux longs cheveux noirs.
Deux anneaux d'argent fin lui pendent aux oreilles,
Et ses yeux sont plus clairs que l'astre des beaux soirs.

Va, sombre messager, dis-lui bien que je l'aime,
Et que voici mon cœur. Elle reconnaîtra
Qu'il est rouge et solide et non tremblant et blême ;
Et la fille d'Ylmer, Corbeau, te sourira !

Moi, je meurs. Mon esprit coule par vingt blessures.
J'ai fait mon temps. Buvez, ô loups, mon sang vermeil.
Jeune, brave, riant, libre et san flétrissures,
Je vais m'asseoir parmi les Dieux, dans le soleil !

"Through Upsàla, where drink the Jarls and sing,
And clash their golden bowls in company,
Bird of the moor, carry on tireless wing
To Ylmer's daughter there the heart of me.

"And thou shalt see her standing straight and pale,
High pedestaled on some rook-haunted tower:
She has two ear-rings, silver and vermeil,
And eyes like stars that shine in sunset hour.

"Tell her my love, thou dark bird ominous;
Give her my heart, no bloodless heart and vile
But red compact and strong, O raven. Thus
Shall Ylmer's daughter greet thee with a smile.

"Now let my life from twenty deep wounds flow,
And wolves may drink the blood. My time is done.
Young, brave and spotless, I rejoice to go
And sit where all the Gods are, in the sun."

(*James Elroy Flecker*)

Charles Baudelaire

1821–1867

. .

CORRESPONDANCES

La Nature est un temple où de vivants piliers
Laissent parfois sortir de confuses paroles;
L'homme y passe à travers des forêts de symboles
Qui l'observent avec des regards familiers.

Comme de longs échos qui de loin se confondent
Dans une ténébreuse et profonde unité,
Vaste comme la nuit et comme la clarté,
Les parfums, les couleurs et les sons se répondent.

Il est des parfums frais comme des chairs d'enfants,
Doux comme les hautbois, verts comme les prairies,
—Et d'autres, corrompus, riches et triomphants,

Ayant l'expansion des choses infinies,
Comme l'ambre, le musc, le benjoin et l'encens,
Qui chantent les transports de l'esprit et des sens.

L'INVITATION AU VOYAGE

Mon enfant, ma sœur,
Songe à la douceur
D'aller là-bas vivre ensemble!
Aimer à loisir,
Aimer et mourir
Au pays qui te ressemble!

Charles Baudelaire

. .

CORRESPONDENCES

ALL NATURE is a temple where the alive
Pillars breathe often a tremor of mixed words;
Man wanders in a forest of accords
That peer familiarly from each ogive.
Like thinning echoes tumbling to sleep beyond
In a unity umbrageous and infinite,
Vast as the night stupendously moonlit,
All smells and colors and sounds correspond.

Odors blown sweet as infants' naked flesh,
Soft as oboes, green as a studded plain,
—Others, corrupt, rich and triumphant, thresh
Expansions to the infinite of pain:
Amber and myrrh, benzoin and musk condense
To transports of the spirit and the sense!

(Allen Tate)

INVITATION TO THE VOYAGE

MY CHILD, my sister, dream
How sweet all things would seem
Were we in that kind land to live together
And there love slow and long,
There love and die among
Those scenes that image you, that sumptuous weather.

Les soleils mouillés
De ces ciels brouillés
Pour mon esprit ont les charmes
Si mystérieux
De tes traîtres yeux,
Brillant à travers leurs larmes.

Là, tout n'est qu'ordre et beauté,
Luxe, calme et volupté.

Des meubles luisants,
Polis par les ans,
Décoreraient notre chambre;
Les plus rares fleurs
Mêlant leurs odeurs
Aux vagues senteurs de l'ambre,
Les riches plafonds,
Les miroirs profonds,
La splendeur orientale,
Tout y parlerait
A l'âme en secret
Sa douce langue natale.

Là, tout n'est qu'ordre et beauté,
Luxe, calme et volupté.

Vois sure ces canaux
Dormir ces vaisseaux
Dont l'humeur est vagabonde;
C'est pour assouvir
Ton moindre désir
Qu'ils viennent du bout du monde.
—Les soleils couchants
Revêtent les champs,

Drowned suns that glimmer there
Through cloud-disheveled air
Move me with such a mystery as appears
Within those other skies
Of your treacherous eyes
When I behold them shining through their tears.

There, there is nothing else but grace and measure,
Richness, quietness, and pleasure.

Furniture that wears
The luster of the years
Softly would glow within our glowing chamber,
Flowers of rarest bloom
Proffering their perfume
Mixed with the vague fragrances of amber;
Gold ceilings would there be,
Mirrors deep as the sea,
The walls all in an Eastern splendor hung—
Nothing but should address
The soul's loneliness,
Speaking her sweet and secret native tongue.

There, there is nothing else but grace and measure,
Richness, quietness, and pleasure.

See, sheltered from the swells
There in the still canals
Those drowsy ships that dream of sailing forth;
It is to satisfy
Your least desire, they ply
Hither through all the waters of the earth.
The sun at close of day
Clothes the fields of hay,

Les canaux, la ville entière,
    D'hyacinthe et d'or ;
    Le monde s'endort

Dans une chaude lumière.
Là, tout n'est qu'ordre et beauté,
Luxe, calme et volupté.

LA MUSIQUE

La musique souvent me prend comme une mer !
    Vers ma pâle étoile,
Sous un plafond de brume ou dans un vaste éther,
    Je mets à la voile ;

La poitrine en avant et les poumons gonflés
    Comme de la toile,
J'escalade le dos des flots amoncelés
    Que la nuit me voile ;

Je sens vibrer en moi toutes les passions
    D'un vaisseau qui souffre ;
Le bon vent, la tempête et ses convulsions

    Sur l'immense gouffre
Me bercent. D'autres fois, calme plat, grand miroir
    De mon désespoir !

Then the canals, at last the town entire
  In hyacinth and gold:
  Slowly the land is rolled
Sleepward under a sea of gentle fire.

There, there is nothing else but grace and measure,
Richness, quietness, and pleasure.

                              (*Richard Wilbur*)

MUSIC

On MUSIC drawn away, a sea-borne mariner
  Star over bowsprit pale,
Beneath a roof of mist or depths of lucid air
  I put out under sail;

Breastbone my steady bow and lungs full, running free
  Before a following gale,
I ride the rolling back and mass of every sea
  By Night wrapt in her veil;

All passions and all joys that vessels undergo
  Tremble alike in me;
Fair winds or waves in havoc when the tempests blow

  On the enormous sea
Rock me, and level calms come silvering sea and air,
  A glass for my despair.

                              (*Robert Fitzgerald*)

PAYSAGE

JE VEUX pour composer chastement mes églogues,
Coucher auprès du ciel, comme les astrologues,
Et, voisin des clochers, écouter en rêvant
Leurs hymnes solennels emportés par le vent.
Les deux mains au menton, du haut de ma mansarde,
Je verrai l'atelier qui chante et qui bavarde;
Les tuyaux, les clochers, ces mâts de la cité,
Et les grands ciels qui font rêver d'éternité.

Il est doux, à travers les brumes, de voir naître
L'étoile dans l'azur, la lampe à la fenêtre,
Les fleuves de charbon monter au firmament
Et la lune verser son pâle enchantement.
Je verrai les printemps, les étés, les automnes,
Et quand viendra l'hiver aux neiges monotones,
Je fermerai partout portières et volets
Pour bâtir dans la nuit mes féeriques palais.

Alors je rêverai des horizons bleuâtres,
Des jardins, des jets d'eau pleurant dans les albâtres,
Des baisers, des oiseaux chantant soir et matin,
Et tout ce que l'Idylle a des plus enfantin.
L'Émeute, tempêtant vainement à ma vitre,
Ne fera pas lever mon front de mon pupitre;
Car je serai plongé dans cette volupté
D'évoquer le Printemps avec ma volonté,
De tirer un soleil de mon cœur, et de faire
De mes pensers brûlants une tiède atmosphère.

LANDSCAPE

I WOULD, more chastely to compose my verse,
Sleep close to the sky, as do astrologers,
And, dreaming neighbor of steeples, attend
Their solemn hymns borne hither by the wind.
Chin in hand, from my frail promontory
I'd watch the shops that sing or tell some story,
The steeples and smokestacks, masts of the city,
Skies in whose depths I dream eternity.

It is sweet to see through mists the brightening glow
Of the star in blue depths, the lamp in the window,
The coal-smoke rivers mounting to the skies,
The moon as she her pale enchantment plies.
I'll see green springs, bright summers, autumns slow,
And then when winter brings monotonous snow,
I'll close the doors and shutters everywhere
And build into the night my palaces of air.

Then shall I dream the blue horizon's shade,
Gardens, weeping fountains of alabaster made,
Kisses, birds that sing as evening and morning strike,
And all the Idyll has that is most childlike.
Though the tumult at my window vainly rages,
I shall not let my eyes stray from these pages.
For I shall be deep in idyllic labor still,
To make the spring come forth by force of will,
To wrench from my own heart a sun entire
And make my own warm climate from my thoughts of fire.

(Henry Taylor)

LA CLOCHE FÊLÉE

Il est amer et doux, pendant les nuits d'hiver,
D'écouter, près du feu qui palpite et qui fume,
Les souvenirs lointains lentement s'élever
Au bruit des carillons qui chantent dans la brume.

Bienheureuse la cloche au gosier vigoureux
Qui, malgré sa vieillesse, alerte et bien portante,
Jette fidèlement son cri religieux,
Ainsi qu'un vieux soldat qui veille sous la tente !

Moi, mon âme est fêlée, et lorsqu'en ses ennuis
Elle veut de ses chants peupler l'air froid des nuits,
Il arrive souvent que sa voix affaiblie

Semble le râle épais d'un blessé qu'on oublie
Au bord d'un lac de sang, sous un grand tas de morts,
Et qui meurt, sans bouger, dans d'immenses efforts !

THE FLAWED BELL

PROPPED on my footstool by the popping log
and sitting out the winter night, I hear
my boyish falsetto crack and disappear
to the sound of the bells jangling through the fog.

Lucky the carrying and loud-tongued bell,
whose metal fights the wear and rust of time
to piously repeat its fractured chime,
like an old trooper playing sentinel!

My soul is flawed, and often when I try
to shrug away my early decrepitude,
and populate the night with my shrill cry,

I hear the death-cough of mortality
choked under corpses by a lake of blood—
my rocklike, unhinging effort to die.

(*Robert Lowell*)

Théodore de Banville

1823–1891

· ·

LE THÉ

MISS ELLEN, versez-moi le Thé
Dans la belle tasse chinoise,
Où des poissons d'or cherchent noise
Au monstre rose épouvanté.

J'aime la folle cruauté
Des chimères qu'on apprivoise :
Miss Ellen, versez-moi le Thé
Dans la belle tasse chinoise.

Là sous un ciel rouge irrité,
Une dame fière et sournoise
Montre en ses longs yeux de turquoise
L'extase et la naïveté :
Miss Ellen, versez-moi le Thé.

Théodore de Banville

. .

TEA

Miss Ellen do, pray, pour the tea
Into this charming Chinese cup,
Where fishes all of gold take up
Their quarrel with a scared pink beast.

I like the wanton cruelty
Of the chimeras one chains up:
Miss Ellen do, pray, pour the tea
Into this charming Chinese cup.

There beneath an angry sky,
A lady, underhand and deep,
Her blue eyes narrow on the cup,
Reveals a naïve ecstasy.
Miss Ellen do, pray, pour the tea.

(*Barbara Howes*)

Charles Cros
1842–1888

· ·

LE HARENG SAUR

Il était un grand mur blanc—nu, nu, nu,
Contre le mur une échelle—haute, haute, haute,
Et, par terre, un hareng saur—sec, sec, sec.

Il vient, tenant dans les mains—sales, sales, sales,
Un marteau lourd, un grand clou—pointu, pointu, pointu,
Un peloton de ficelle—gros, gros, gros.

Alors il monte à l'échelle—haute, haute, haute,
Et plante le clou pointu—toc, toc, toc,
Tout en haut du grand mur blanc—nu, nu, nu.

Il laisse aller le marteau—qui tombe, qui tombe, qui tombe,
Attache au clou la ficelle—longue, longue, longue,
Et, au bout, le hareng saur—sec, sec, sec.

Il redescend l'échelle—haute, haute, haute,
L'emporte avec le marteau—lourd, lourd, lourd,
Et puis, il s'en va ailleurs—loin, loin, loin.

Et, depuis, le hareng saur,—sec, sec, sec,
Au bout de cette ficelle—longue, longue, longue,
Très lentement se balance—toujours, toujours, toujours.

J'ai composé cette histoire—simple, simple, simple,
Pour mettre en fureur les gens—graves, graves, graves,
Et amuser les enfants—petits, petits, petits.

Charles Cros

. .

THE SMOKED HERRING

THERE was a great white wall—bare, bare, bare,
Against the wall a ladder—high, high, high,
And, on the ground, a smoked herring—dry, dry, dry,

He comes, bearing in his hands—so dirty, dirty, dirty,
A heavy hammer, a great nail—sharp, sharp, sharp,
A ball of string—so big, big, big.

Then he climbs the ladder—high, high, high,
And drives the pointed nail—toc, toc, toc,
Into the top of the great white wall—bare, bare, bare.

He lets the hammer go—it falls, falls, falls,
Ties to the nail the string—so long, long, long,
And, to the end, the smoked herring—dry, dry, dry.

He descends the ladder—so high, high, high,
Carries it away, with the hammer—so heavy, heavy, heavy,
And so he goes away—far, far, far.

And ever since the smoked herring—dry, dry, dry,
At the end of the string—so long, long, long,
Very slowly swings—for ever, ever, ever.

I have made up this little tale—so simple, simple, simple,
Just to enrage people—so grave, grave, grave,
And to amuse children—so small, small, small.

(*A. L. Lloyd*)

Stéphane Mallarmé

1842–1898

. .

LE VIERGE, LE VIVACE ET LE BEL AUJOURD'HUI

LE VIERGE, le vivace et le bel aujourd'hui
Va-t-il nous déchirer avec un coup d'aile ivre
Ce lac dur oublié que hante sous le givre
Le transparent glacier des vols qui n'ont pas fui !

Un cygne d'autrefois se souvient que c'est lui
Magnifique mais qui sans espoir se délivre
Pour n'avoir pas chanté la région où vivre
Quand du stérile hiver a resplendi l'ennui.

Tout son col secouera cette blanche agonie
Par l'espace infligée à l'oiseau qui le nie,
Mais non l'horreur du sol où le plumage est pris.

Fantôme qu'à ce lieu son pur éclat assigne,
Il s'immobilise au songe froid du mépris
Que vêt parmi l'exil inutile le Cygne.

SOUPIR

MON ÂME vers ton front où rêve, ô calme sœur,
Un automne jonché de taches de rousseur,
Et vers le ciel errant de ton œil angélique
Monte, comme dans un jardin mélancolique,
Fidèle, un blanc jet d'eau soupire vers l'Azur !
—Vers l'Azur attendri d'Octobre pâle et pur
Qui mire aux grands bassins sa langueur infinie
Et laisse, sur l'eau morte où la fauve agonie
Des feuilles erre au vent et creuse un froid sillon,
Se traîner le soleil jaune d'un long rayon.

Stéphane Mallarmé

. .

THE VIRGIN, BRIGHT, AND BEAUTIFUL TO-DAY

THE VIRGIN, bright, and beautiful to-day
Dare it now shatter with a drunken wing
This hard, forgotten lake, this ice where cling
These flights of mine that never flew away . . .
Once was a swan, remembers it is he,
Magnificent but hopeless in his strife,
For never having sung the realms of life
When winter shone in bleak sterility.
His neck in a white agony is shaken,
Shattering the space that mocks him for his pride
But not the soil in which his plumes are taken.
Phantom mere brightness to this scene has drawn,
Immobile in the cold, where dreams deride,
Clothed in the useless exile of the swan.

(G. S. Fraser)

SIGH

MY SOUL, oh peaceful sister, toward your brow where dreams
An autumn littered with its freckled russet gleams,
And toward the wandering sky of your angelic eyes,
Ascends, as in a melancholy garden sighs,
Faithful, a silver fountain upward to the Azure!
—Toward the soft October Azure, pale and pure,
That watches in great pools its boundless languor flow,
And lets, on the stagnant water where the tawny throes
Of leaves drift in the wind and dig a chilly grave,
The yellow sun drag slowly by a long ray.

(Hubert Creekmore)

José Maria de Heredia

1842–1905

. .

LE NAUFRAGÉ

Avec la brise en poupe et par un ciel serein,
Voyant le Phare fuir à travers la mâture,
Il est parti d'Égypte au lever de l'Arcture,
Fier de sa nef rapide aux flancs doublés d'airain.

Il ne reverra plus le môle Alexandrin.
Dans le sable où pas même un chevreau ne pâture
La tempête a creusé sa triste sépulture ;
Le vent du large y tord quelque arbuste marin.

Au pli le plus profond de la mouvante dune,
En la nuit sans aurore et sans astre et sans lune,
Que le navigateur trouve enfin le repos.

O Terre, ô Mer, pitié pour son Ombre anxieuse !
Et sur la rive hellène où sont venus ses os,
Soyez-lui, toi, légère, et toi, silencieuse.

ANTOINE ET CLÉOPATRE

Tous deux ils regardaient, de la haute terrasse,
L'Égypte s'endormir sous un ciel étouffant
Et le Fleuve, à travers le Delta noir qu'il fend,
Vers Bubaste ou Saïs rouler son onde grasse.

José Maria de Heredia

· ·

THE LOST SAILOR

A FOLLOWING breeze, Arcturus clear of clouds,
He watched the Pharos fading through the shrouds,
The coast of Egypt vanish from his view,
Proud of his buoyant ship, with bronze made new.

O nevermore the lights of home for her!
On desert dunes where not a blade can grow
And through the tamarisk the sad winds blow,
The storm itself has dug his sepulchre.

Deep in the hollow of the shifting sands
Make still at last his troubled heart and hands,
And in the starless, moonless, dawnless night
Grant to a ship-wrecked mariner his right.

There on that Grecian shore, become his grave,
Give to his wandering ghost, what all ghosts crave;
Cover him lightly earth, and hush him, wave.

(*Frances Cornford*)

ANTONY AND CLEOPATRA

THE LOVERS pace the terrace nervously,
See Egypt dream beneath a sultry sky,
And hear the Nile, ambitious serpent, sigh
Through Saïs and Bubastis for the sea.

Et le Romain sentait sous sa lourde cuirasse,
Soldat captif berçant le sommeil d'un enfant,
Ployer et défaillir sur son cœur triomphant
Le corps voluptueux que son étreinte embrasse.

Tournant sa tête pâle entre ses cheveux bruns
Vers celui qu'enivraient d'invincibles parfums,
Elle tendit sa bouche et ses prunelles claires;

Et sur elle courbé, l'ardent Imperator
Vit dans ses larges yeux étoilés de points d'or
Toute une mer immense où fuyaient des galères.

The Roman feels beneath his stout cuirass—
Captive soldier cradled like a child—
Bending on his triumphant heart, the wild,
Barbaric body golden as his brass.

Turning her white face in its dark frame
Of hair to him, drunk with her wild perfume,
She offers up her lips and liquid eyes.

The Imperator bends to take his prize,
Sees in those gold-flecked eyes a troubled sea,
Immense and dark, where broken galleys flee.

(*Henri Coulette*)

Paul Verlaine

1844–1896

. .

COLOMBINE

LÉANDRE le sot
Pierrot qui d'un saut
    De puce
Franchit le buisson,
Cassandre sous son
    Capuce,

Arlequin aussi,
Cet aigrefin si
    Fantasque,
Aux costumes fous
Ses yeux luisants sous
    Son masque,

—Do, mi, sol, mi, fa,—
Tout ce monde va,
    Rit, chante
Et danse devant
Une belle enfant
    Méchante

Dont les yeux pervers
Comme les yeux verts
    Des chattes
Gardent ses appas
Et disent: "A bas
    Les pattes !"

Paul Verlaine

. .

COLOMBINE

THE FOOLISH Leander
Cape-covered Cassander
And which
Is Pierrot? 'tis he
With the hop of a flea
Leaps the ditch;

And Harlequin who
Rehearses anew
His sly task,
With his dress that's a wonder,
And eyes shining under
His mask;

Mi, sol, mi, fa, do!
How gaily they go,
And they sing
And they laugh and they twirl
Round the feet of a girl
Like the Spring,

Whose eyes are as green
As a cat's are, and keen
As its claws,
And her eyes without frown
Bid all newcomers: Down
With your paws!

—Eux ils vont toujours !—
Fatidique cours
    Des astres,
Oh ! dis-moi vers quels
Mornes ou cruels
    Désastres

L'implacable enfant,
Preste et relevant
    Ses jupes
La rose au chapeau,
Conduit son troupeau
    De dupes !

LE CIEL EST, PAR-DESSUS LE TOIT

Le ciel est, par-dessus le toit,
    Si bleu, si calme !
Un arbre, par-dessus le toit,
    Berce sa palme.

La cloche, dans le ciel qu'on voit,
    Doucement tinte.
Un oiseau sur l'arbre qu'on voit
    Chante sa plainte.

Mon Dieu, mon Dieu, la vie est là,
    Simple et tranquille.
Cette paisible rumeur-là
    Vient de la ville.

On they go with the force
Of the stars in their course,
And the speed:
O tell me toward what
Disaster unthought,
Without heed

The implacable fair
A rose in her hair,
Holding up
Her skirts as she runs
Leads this dance of the dunce
And the dupe?

(*Arthur Symons*)

THE SKY IS UP ABOVE THE ROOF

THE SKY is up above the roof
  So blue, so soft.
A tree there, up above the roof,
  Swayeth aloft.

A bell within that sky we see,
  Chimes low and faint;
A bird upon that tree we see,
  Maketh complaint.

Dear God, is not the life up there
  Simple and sweet?
How peacefully are borne up there
  Sounds of the street.

—Qu'as-tu fait, ô toi que voilà
Pleurant sans cesse,
Dis, qu'as-tu fait, toi que voilà,
De ta jeunesse?

COLLOQUE SENTIMENTALE

Dans le vieux parc solitaire et glacé
Deux formes ont tout à l'heure passé.

Leurs yeux sont morts et leurs lèvres sont molles,
Et l'on entend à peine leurs paroles.

Dans le vieux parc solitaire et glacé
Deux spectres ont évoqué le passé.

—Te souviens-tu de notre extase ancienne?
—Pourquoi voulez-vous donc qu'il m'en souvienne?

—Ton cœur bat-il toujours à mon seul nom?
Toujours vois-tu mon âme en rêve?—Non.

—Ah! les beaux jours de bonheur indicible
Où nous joignions nos bouches!—C'est possible.

—Qu'il était beau le ciel, et grand, l'espoir!
—L'espoir a fui, vaincu, vers le ciel noir.

Tels ils marchaient dans les avoines folles,
Et la nuit seule entendit leurs paroles.

What hast thou done, who comest here,
  To weep alway?
Where hast thou laid, who comest here,
  Thy youth away?

(*Ernest Dowson*)

COLLOQUE SENTIMENTALE

IN THE old park, solitary and vast,
Over the frozen ground two forms once passed.

Their lips were languid and their eyes were dead,
And hardly could be heard the words they said.

In the old park, solitary and vast,
Two ghosts once met to summon up the past.

—Do you remember our old ecstasy?
—Why would you bring it back again to me?

—Do you still dream as you dreamed long ago?
Does your heart beat to my heart's beating?—No.

—Ah, those old days, what joys have those days seen
When your lips met my lips!—It may have been.

—How blue the sky was, and our hope how light!
—Hope has flown helpless back into the night.

They walked through weeds withered and grasses dead
And only the night heard the words they said.

(*Arthur Symons*)

LE PIANO QUE BAISE UNE MAIN FRÊLE

Le piano que baise une main frêle
Luit dans le soir rose et gris vaguement,
Tandis qu'avec un très léger bruit d'aile
Un air bien vieux, bien faible et bien charmant
Rôde discret, épeuré quasiment,
Par le boudoir longtemps parfumé d'Elle.

Qu'est-ce que c'est que ce berceau soudain
Qui lentement dorlote mon pauvre être?
Que voudrais-tu de moi, doux chant badin?
Qu'as-tu voulu, fin refrain incertain
Qui vas tantôt mourir vers la fenêtre
Ouverte un peu sur le petit jardin?

CHANSON D'AUTOMNE

Les sanglots longs
Des violons
   De l'automne
Blessent mon cœur
D'une langueur
   Monotone.

Tout suffocant
Et blême, quand
   Sonne l'heure,
Je me souviens
Des jours anciens
   Et je pleure.

THE PIANO

THE PIANO, kissed by hands not sure nor strong,
 Shines dimly in the rose-grey evening air,
The while a well-remembered charming song,
 Whose wavering wings its half-heard whispers bear,
 With fearful-seeming pauses here and there,
Steals round the chamber that was Hers so long.

What is this sudden strain that brings repose
 In lingering cadence on my languid eyes?
What means the playful air, that floats and flows?
 Why seeks it me, the tune that softly rose,
 And on the way towards the window dies,
Half-open on the little garden-close?

(*Edward Marsh*)

SONG OF AUTUMN

WHEN a sighing begins
In the violins
Of the autumn-song,
My heart is drowned
In the slow sound
Languorous and long.

Pale as with pain,
Breath fails me when
The hour tolls deep.
My thoughts recover
The days that are over,
And I weep.

Et je m'en vais
Au vent mauvais
    Qui m'emporte
Deci, delà,
Pareil à la
    Feuille morte.

LE ROSSIGNOL

COMME un vol criard d'oiseaux en émoi,
Tous mes souvenirs s'abattent sur moi,
S'abattent parmi le feuillage jaune
De mon cœur mirant son tronc plié d'aune
Au tain violet de l'eau des Regrets
Qui mélancoliquement coule auprès,
S'abattent, et puis la rumeur mauvaise
Qu'une brise moite en montant apaise,
S'éteint par degrés dans l'arbre, si bien
Qu'au bout d'un instant on n'entend plus rien,
Plus rien que la voix célébrant l'Absente.
Plus rien que la voix—ô si languissante!—
De l'oiseau que fut mon Premier Amour,
Et qui chante encore comme au premier jour;
Et dans la splendeur triste d'une lune
Se levant blafarde et solennelle, une
Nuit mélancolique et lourde d'été,
Pleine de silence et d'obscurité,
Berce sur l'azur qu'un vent doux effleure
L'arbre qui frissonne et l'oiseau qui pleure.

And I go
Where the winds know,
Broken and brief,
To and fro,
As the winds blow
A dead leaf.

(Arthur Symons)

THE NIGHTINGALE

LIKE a clamorous flock of birds in alarm,
All my memories descend and take form,
Descend through the yellow foliage of my heart
That watches its trunk of alder twist apart,
To the violet foil of the water of remorse
Which nearby runs its melancholy course,
Descend, and then the malevolent cries
Which a damp wind, rising, pacifies,
Die slowly away in the trees, and before
An instant has passed I hear nothing more,
Nothing more than the voice that sings what is lost.
Nothing more than the voice—oh, voice of a ghost!—
Of my earliest love, the voice of a bird
Who sings as he sang the first day he was heard;
And in the solemnity and pallor
Of a moon rising in sorrowful splendor,
A summer night, melancholic and heavy,
Heavy with silence and obscurity,
Lulls on the sky that a soft wind sweeps
The tree that trembles and the bird that weeps.

(Henry Taylor)

Tristan Corbière

1845–1875

. .

LE CRAPAUD

UN CHANT dans une nuit sans air...
—La lune plaque en métal clair
Les découpures du vert sombre.

... Un chant; comme un écho, tout vif
Enterré, là, sous le massif...
—Ça se tait. Viens, c'est là, dans l'ombre...

—Un crapaud!—Pourquoi cette peur,
Près de moi, ton soldat fidèle!
Vois-le, poète tondu, sans aile,
Rossignol de la boue...—Horreur!—

...—Il chante.—Horreur!!—Horreur pourquoi?
Vois-tu pas son œil de lumière?...
Non: il s'en va, froid, sous sa pierre.
Bonsoir—Ce crapaud-là, c'est moi.

Tristan Corbière

. .

THE TOAD

A SONG in a windless night . . .
—The moon plates in metal bright
The cut-out images of dark green.

. . . A song; sudden as an echo, quick,
Buried, there, under the thick
Clump. It stops. Come, it's there, unseen . . .

—A toad!—There in shadow.—Why this terror
Near me, your faithful soldier?—Spring!—
Look at him, poet clipped, no wing,
Nightingale of the mud . . .—Horror!—

. . .—He sings.—Horror!!—Horror! But why?
Don't you see that eye of light, his own?
No: he goes, chilled, beneath his stone.
Good-night. That toad you heard is I.

(Vernon Watkins)

ÉPITAPHE
pour Tristan-Joachim-Edouard Corbière, philosophe
épave, mort-né

Mêlange adultère de tout:
De la fortune et pas le sou,
De l'énergie et pas de force,
La Liberté, mais une entorse.
Du coeur, du coeur! de l'âme, non—
Des amis, pas un compagnon,
De l'idée et pas une idée,
De l'amour et pas une aimée,
La paresse et pas le repos.
Vertus chez lui furent défaut,
Ame blasée inassouvie.
Mort, mais pas guéri de la vie,
Gâcheur de vie hors de propos,
Le corps à sec et la tête ivre,
Espérant, niant l'avenir,
Il mourut en s'attendant vivre
Et vécut s'attendant mourir.

EPITAPH
for *Tristan-Joachim-Edouard Corbière, Philosopher,*
Stray, Stillborn

MONGREL bred of every strain:
Born to wealth, not a cent to his name,
Energy enough but strength lacking,
Free to move, but with a foot dragging.
A heart, what a heart! but spirit, none—
Plenty of friends, not one companion,
Full of ideals but of ideas, empty,
Of love but unloved by anybody,
Idleness always and never rest.
Virtues in him became defects;
Sated, still he was unsatisfied.
Not yet cured of life when he died,
Wasting his life to no good end,
Body dried out and head aswim,
Hoping, but every hope denied,
He died in readiness to live
And lived in readiness to die.

(*Walter McElroy*)

Arthur Rimbaud

1854–1891

. .

SENSATION

PAR LES SOIRS bleus d'été, j'irai dans les sentiers,
Picoté par les blés, fouler l'herbe menue:
Rêveur, j'en sentirai la fraîcheur à mes pieds,
Je laisserai le vent baigner ma tête nue!

Je ne parlerai pas, je ne penserai rien:
Mais l'amour infini me montera dans l'âme,
Et j'irai loin, bien loin, comme un bohémien,
Par la Nature,—heureux comme avec une femme.

VOYELLES

A NOIR, E blanc, I rouge, U vert, O bleu, voyelles
Je dirai quelque jour vos naissances latentes
A, noir corset velu des mouches éclatantes
Qui bombinent autour des puanteurs cruelles,

Golfe d'ombre; E, candeur des vapeurs et des tentes,
Lance des glaciers fiers, rois blancs, frissons d'ombelle;
I, pourpres, sang craché, rire des lèvres belles
Dans la colère ou les ivresses pénitentes;

Arthur Rimbaud

.   .

SENSATION

ON SUMMER evenings blue, pricked by the wheat
   On rustic paths the thin grass I shall tread,
And feel its freshness underneath my feet,
   And, dreaming, let the wind bathe my bare head.

I shall not speak, nor think, but, walking slow
   Through Nature, I shall rove with Love my guide,
As gypsies wander, where, they do not know,
   Happy as one walks by a woman's side.

(*Jethro Bithell*)

VOWELS

A BLACK, E white, I red, U green, O blue—I'll tell
One day, you vowels how you came to be and whence.
A, black, the glittering of flies that form a dense,
Velvety corset round some foul and cruel smell,

Gulf of dark shadow; E, the glacier's insolence,
Steams, tents, white kings, the quiver of a flowery bell;
I, crimsons, blood expectorated, laughs that well
From lovely lips in wrath or drunken penitence;

U, cycles, vibrements divins des mers virides,
Paix des pâtis semés d'animaux, paix des rides
Que l'alchimie imprime aux grands fronts studieux;

O, suprême Clairon plein des strideurs étranges,
Silences traversés des Mondes et des Anges:
—O l'Oméga, rayon violet de Ses Yeux!

MARINE

LES CHARS d'argent et de cuivre—
Les proues d'acier et d'argent—
Battent l'écume,—
Soulèvent les souches des ronces.

Les courants de la lande,
Et les ornières immenses du reflux,
Filent circulairement vers l'est,
Vers les piliers de la forêt,
Vers les fûts de la jetée,
Dont l'angle est heurté par des tourbillons de lumière.

U, cycles, the divine vibrations of the seas,
Peace of herb-dotted pastures or the wrinkled ease
That alchemy imprints upon the scholar's brow;

O, the last trumpet, loud with strangely strident brass
The silences through which the words and angels pass:
O stands for Omega, His Eyes' deep violet glow!

(*Norman Cameron*)

MARINE

THE CHARIOTS of silver and copper,
The prows of steel and silver
Beat foam
And lift up the stumps of the bramble.

The currents of the heath
And the immense ruts delved by their reflux
Veer in a circle to the east,
Toward the pillars of the forest,
Toward the piles of the jetty,
Whose angle is struck by the whirlwinds of light.

(*Francis Golffing*)

MA BOHÈME

Je m'en allais, les poings dans mes poches crevées ;
Mon paletot aussi devenait idéal ;
J'allais sous le ciel, Muse ! et j'étais ton féal ;
Oh ! là là ! que d'amours splendides j'ai rêvées !

Mon unique culotte avait un large trou.
—Petit-Poucet rêveur, j'égrenais dans ma course
Des rimes. Mon auberge était à la Grande-Ourse.
—Mes étoiles au ciel avaient un doux frou-frou

Et je les écoutais, assis au bord des routes,
Ces bons soirs de septembre où je sentais des gouttes
De rosée à mon front, comme un vin de vigueur ;

Où, rimant au milieu des ombres fantastiques,
Comme des lyres, je tirais les élastiques
De mes souliers blessés, un pied près de mon cœur !

LARME

Loin des oiseaux, des troupeaux, des villageoises,
Que buvais-je, à genoux dans cette bruyère
Entourée de tendres bois de noisetiers,
Dans un brouillard d'après-midi tiède et vert ?

Que pouvais-je boire dans cette jeune Oise,
—Ormeaux sans voix, gazon sans fleurs, ciel couvert !—
Boire à ces gourdes jaunes, loin de ma case
Chérie ? Quelque liqueur d'or qui fait suer.

THE STROLLING PLAYER

MY HANDS in pockets worn out at the seams,
And clad in a coat that was almost perfect, too,
I traveled, Muse, and I was true to you;
How splendid were the loves I found in dreams!

I had a large hole in my pants, my only pair.
Like Tom Thumb, dreamer lad, I formed my rhymes;
I stayed at the Sign of the Dipper several times.
My stars made a sound like silk in the high, night air.

I'd hear them on the highway when I stopped
Those good September evenings while dew dropped,
Cooling my head like wine poured in the dark;

When rhyming in those shadowed, eerie places,
Like lyre strings I'd pluck the elastic laces
Of my battered shoes, one foot against my heart.

(*William Jay Smith*)

LARME

FAR from the birds, the herds, the village girls
What did I drink, in heather to my knees,
Within a tender grove of walnut trees
In the warm green mist of an afternoon?

What could I drink in that young stream,
—Tuneless reeds, flowerless grass, cloudy sky!—
Drink from those yellow gourds, far from the dreamed of
Hut? Gold that drunk brought sweat to the skin.

Je faisais une louche enseigne d'auberge.
—Un orage vint chasser le ciel. Au soir
L'eau des bois se perdait sur les sables vierges,
Le vent de Dieu jetait des glaçons aux mares;

Pleurant, je voyais de l'or—et ne pus boire.

I might have swayed a queer sign for an inn.
—A long wind swept the clouds away. That night
The waters of the wood were sunk in sands
And a wind from God flung glass on all the ponds.

Weeping, I saw the gold—and could not drink.

(*John Peale Bishop*)

Jean Moréas

1856–1910

. .

Extrait de *STANCES*

La rose du jardin que j'avais méprisée
A cause de son simple et modeste contour,
Sans se baigner d'azur, sans humer la rosée,
Dans le vase, captive, a vécu plus d'un jour.

Puis lasse, abandonnée à ces pâleurs fatales,
Ayant fini d'éclore et de s'épanouir,
Elle laisse tomber lentement ses pétales,
Indifférente au soin de vivre ou de mourir.

Lorsque l'obscur destin passe, sachons nous taire.
Pourquoi ce souvenir que j'emporte aujourd'hui?
Mon cœur est trop chargé d'ombres et de mystère;
Le spectre d'une fleur est un fardeau pour lui.

Jean Moréas

. .

From *STANCES*

The garden rose I paid no honour to,
So humbly poised and fashioned on its spray,
Has now by wind unkissed, undrenched by dew,
Lived captive in her vase beyond a day.

And tired and pale, bereft of earth and sun,
Her blossom over and her hour of pride,
She dropped down all her petals, one by one,
Unmindful if she lived or how she died.

When doom is passing in her dusky glade
Let us learn silence. In this evening hour,
O heart bowed down with mystery and shade,
Too heavy lies the spectre of a flower!

(*James Elroy Flecker*)

Jules Laforgue

1860–1887

. .

L'IMPOSSIBLE

Je puis mourir ce soir ! Averses, vents, soleil
Distribueront partout mon cœur, mes nerfs, mes moelles.
Tout sera dit pour moi ! Ni rêve, ni réveil.
Je n'aurai pas été là-bas, dans les étoiles !

En tous sens, je le sais, sur ces mondes lointains,
Pèlerins comme nous des pâles solitudes,
Dans la douceur des nuits tendant vers nous les mains,
Des Humanités sœurs rêvent par multitudes !

Oui ! des frères partout ! (Je le sais, je la sais !)
Ils sont seuls comme nous.—Palpitants de tristesse,
La nuit, ils nous font signe ! Ah ! n'irons-nous, jamais?
On se consolerait dans la grande détresse !

Les astres, c'est certain, un jour s'aborderont !
Peut-être alors luira l'Aurore universelle
Que nous chantent ces gueux qui vont, l'Idée au front !
Ce sera contre Dieu la clameur fraternelle !

Hélas ! avant ces temps, averses, vents, soleil
Auront au loin perdu mon cœur, mes nerfs, mes moelles,
Tout se fera sans moi ! Ni rêve, ni réveil !
Je n'aurai pas été dans les douces étoiles !

Jules Laforgue

. .

THE IMPOSSIBLE

TONIGHT I may die. Rain, wind, sun
Will scatter everywhere my heart, my nerves, my marrow.
All will be over for me. Neither sleep nor awakening.
I shall not have been out there among the stars.

In every direction, I know, on those distant worlds,
Are similar pilgrims of pale solitudes,
Extending us their hands across the gentle dark,
Sister Humanities dreaming in multitudes.

Yes, brothers everywhere. That I know, I know.
And all alone like us. Trembling with sadness,
They beckon to us at night. Ah, shall we never go?
We would console one another in our great distress.

The stars, it is certain, will one day meet,
Heralding perhaps that universal dawn
Now sung by those beggars with caste marks of thought.
A fraternal outcry will be raised against God.

Alas, before that time, rain, wind, sun
Will have lost in the distance my heart, my nerves, my marrow.
All will be done without me. Neither dream nor awakening.
I shall not have been among the gentle stars.

(*William Jay Smith*)

AVERTISSEMENT

MON PÈRE (un dur par timidité)
Est mort avec un profil sévère;
J'avais presque pas connu ma mère.
Et donc vers vingt ans je suis resté.

Alors, j'ai fait d'la littérature,
Mais le Démon de la Vérité
Sifflotait tout l'temps à mes côtés:
"Pauvre! as-tu fini tes écritures..."

Or, pas le cœur de me marier,
Étant, moi, au fond, trop méprisable!
Et elles, pas assez intraitables!!
Mais tout l'temps là à s'extasier!...

C'est pourquoi je vivotte, vivotte,
Bonne girouette aux trent'-six saisons,
Trop nombreux pour dire oui ou non...
—Jeunes gens! que je vous serv' d'Ilote!

FOREWORD

MY FATHER, severe because he was shy,
Met his death with a solid jaw;
My mother I hardly ever saw:
At twenty life had passed me by.

And so before long I began to write,
But the Devil of Truth who hovered near
Would lean and whistle in my ear:
"Enough, poor fool, put out the light."

And being as hateful as they come,
I had no heart for marital bliss;
Women so readily say yes,
And stand entranced like the deaf and dumb.

You can understand why my life has been
A weathervane in the blowing breeze,
Changing its tune with perfect ease.
I speak for all you fine young men.

(*William Jay Smith*)

Paul-Jean Toulet

1867–1920

. .

CONTRERIMES

XLIV

Vous qui retournez du Cathai
  Par les Messageries,
Quand vous berçaient à leurs féeries
  L'opium ou le thé,

Dans un palais d'aventurine
  Où se mourait le jour,
Avez-vous vu Boudroulboudour,
  Princesse de la Chine,

Plus blanche en son pantalon noir
  Que nacre sous l'écaille?
Au clair de lune, Jean Chicaille,
  Vous est-il venu voir,

En pleurant comme l'asphodèle
  Aux îles d'Ouac-Wac,
Et jurer de coudre en un sac
  Son épouse infidèle,

Mais telle qu'à travers le vent
  Des mers sur le rivage
S'envole et brille un paon sauvage
  Dans le soleil levant?

145

Paul-Jean Toulet

. .

CATHAY

YOU who have from far Cathay
By perilous convoy come,
While under the spell of opium
Or drunk with tea

In the palace of some paramour
When day dies in the west,
Did you then gaze upon Princess
Boudroulboudour

Whiter than luminous abalone
In her black pantaloon;
And then one night beneath the moon
Did John Chinee

Knock at your door, as bowed in grief
As the asphodel of Ouac,
And vow he'd sew up in a sack
His lovely wife

Who, though unfaithful, still was one
Who could from wind-swept rock
Rise, a shimmering white peacock,
In the rising sun?

(*William Jay Smith*)

Edmond Rostand

1868–1918

. .

BALLADE
Extrait de *Cyrano de Bergerac*

JE JETTE avec grâce mon feutre,
Je fais lentement l'abandon
Du grand manteau qui me calfeutre,
Et je tire mon espadon;
Elégant comme Céladon;
Agile comme Scaramouche,
Je vous préviens, cher Myrmidon,
Qu'à la fin de l'envoi, je touche.

Vous auriez bien dû rester neutre;
Où vais-je larder, dindon?...
Dans le flanc, sous votre maheutre?...
Au cœur, sous votre bleu cordon?...
—Les coquilles tintent, ding-don!
Ma pointe voltige: une mouche!
Décidément...c'est au bedon,
Qu'à la fin de l'envoi, je touche.

Il me manque une rime en eutre...
Vous rompez, plus blanc qu'amidon?
C'est pour me fournir le mot pleutre!
—Tac! je pare la pointe dont
Vous espériez me faire don,—
J'ouvre la ligne,—je la bouche...
Tiens bien ta broche, Laridon!
A la fin de l'envoi, je touche.

Edmond Rostand

. .

BALLADE
From *Cyrano de Bergerac*

MY HAT is flung swiftly away;
My cloak is thrown off, if you please;
And my sword, always eager to play,
Flies out of the scabbard I seize.
My sword, I confess, is a tease,
With a nimble and mischievous brain;
And it knows, as the blade makes a breeze,
I shall strike as I end the refrain.

You should have kept quiet today.
I could carve you, my friend, by degrees.
But where? For a start, shall we say
In the side? Or the narrowest squeeze
'Twixt your ribs, while your arteries freeze,
And my point makes a sly meaning plain?
Guard that paunch! You're beginning to wheeze!
I shall strike as I end the refrain.

I need a word rhyming with *a*,
For, look, you turn paler than cheese
And whiter than—there's the word!—clay.
Your weak thrusts I parry with ease;
Too late now to pause or appease.
Hold on to your spit, though in pain,
For—if you'll permit the reprise—
I shall strike as I end the refrain.

Prince, demande à Dieu pardon!
Je quarte du pied, j'escarmouche,
Je coupe, je feinte...Hé! là donc!
A la fin de l'envoi, je touche.

Francis Jammes

1868–1938

. .

PRIÈRE POUR ALLER AU PARADIS
AVEC LES ÂNES

LORSQU'IL faudra aller vers vous, ô mon Dieu, faites
que ce soit par un jour où la campagne en fête
poudroiera. Je désire, ainsi que je fis ici-bas,
choisir un chemin pour aller, comme il me plaira,
au Paradis, où sont en plein jour les étoiles.
Je prendrai mon bâton et sur la grande route
j'irai, et je dirai aux ânes, mes amis:
"Je suis Francis Jammes et je vais au Paradis,
car il n'y a pas d'enfer au pays du Bon-Dieu."
Je leur dirai: "Venez, doux amis du ciel bleu,
pauvres bêtes chéries qui, d'un brusque mouvement d'oreille,
chassez les mouches plates, les coups et les abeilles…"

Que je Vous apparaisse au milieu de ces bêtes
que j'aime tant parce qu'elles baissent la tête
doucement, et s'arrêtent en joignant leurs petits pieds
d'une façon bien douce et qui vous fait pitié.

Pray God, prince, to pardon all these
Poor efforts of yours, all in vain.
I thrust as you sink to your knees;
And I strike—as I end the refrain !

(*Louis Untermeyer*)

Francis Jammes

. .

A PRAYER TO GO TO PARADISE
WITH THE DONKEYS

WHEN I must come to you, O my God, I pray
It be some dusty-roaded holiday,
And even as in my travels here below,
I beg to choose by what road I shall go
To Paradise, where the clear stars shine by day.
I'll take my walking-stick and go my way,
And to my friends the donkeys I shall say,
"I am Francis Jammes, and I'm going to Paradise,
For there is no hell in the land of the loving God."
And I'll say to them: "Come, sweet friends of the blue skies,
Poor creatures who with a flap of the ears or a nod
Of the head shake off the buffets, the bees, the flies . . ."

Let me come with these donkeys, Lord, into your land,
These beasts who bow their heads so gently, and stand
With their small feet joined together in a fashion
Utterly gentle, asking your compassion.

J'arriverai suivi de leurs milliers d'oreilles,
suivi de ceux qui portèrent au flanc des corbeilles,
de ceux traînant des voitures de saltimbanques
ou des voitures de plumeaux et de fer-blanc,
de ceux qui ont au dos des bidons bossués,
des ânesses pleines comme des outres, aux pas cassés,
de ceux à qui l'on met de petits pantalons
à cause des plaies bleues et suintantes que font
les mouches entêtées qui s'y groupent en ronds.
Mon Dieu, faites qu'avec ces ânes je Vous vienne.
Faites que, dans la paix, des anges nous conduisent
vers des ruisseaux touffus où tremblent des cerises
lisses comme la chair qui rit des jeunes filles,
et faites que, penché dans ce séjour des âmes,
sur vos divines eaux, je sois pareil aux ânes
qui mireront leur humble et douce pauvreté
à la limpidité de l'amour éternel.

Paul Claudel

1868–1955

. .

L'ENFANT JÉSUS DE PRAGUE

IL NEIGE. Le grand monde est mort sans doute. C'est décembre.
Mais qu'il fait bon, mon Dieu, dans la petite chambre !
La cheminée emplie de charbons rougeoyants
Colore le plafond d'un reflet somnolent,
Et l'on n'entend que l'eau qui bout à petit bruit.

I shall arrive, followed by their thousands of ears,
Followed by those with baskets at their flanks,
By those who lug the carts of mountebanks
Or loads of feather-dusters and kitchen-wares,
By those with humps of battered water-cans,
By bottle-shaped she-asses who halt and stumble,
By those tricked out in little pantaloons
To cover their wet, blue galls where flies assemble
In whirling swarms, making a drunken hum.
Dear God, let it be with these donkeys that I come,
And let it be that angels lead us in peace
To leafy streams where cherries tremble in air,
Sleek as the laughing flesh of girls; and there
In that haven of souls let it be that, leaning above
Your divine waters, I shall resemble these donkeys,
Whose humble and sweet poverty will appear
Clear in the clearness of your eternal love.

(Richard Wilbur)

Paul Claudel

. .

THE CHILD JESUS OF PRAGUE

IT SNOWS, and out of doors perhaps the world has died.
It is December, but how good it is inside
Here in this quiet room, before the sleepy glow
Of ruddy coals that fill the fireplace, and throw
Warm lights across the ceiling. Every sound is stilled,

La-haut sur l'étagère, au-dessus des deux lits,
Sous son globe de verre, couronne en tête,
L'une des mains tenant le monde, l'autre prête
A couvrir ces petits qui se confient à elle,
Tout aimable dans sa grande robe solennelle
Et magnifique sous cet énorme chapeau jaune,
L'Enfant Jésus de Prague règne et trône.
Il est tout seul devant le foyer qui l'éclaire
Comme l'hostie cachée au fond du sanctuaire,
L'Enfant-Dieu jusqu'au jour garde ses petits frères.
Inentendue comme le souffle qui s'exhale,
L'existence éternelle emplit la chambre, égale
A toutes ces pauvres choses innocentes et naïves !
Quand il est avec nous, nul mal ne nous arrive.
On peut dormir, Jésus notre frère, est ici.
Il est à nous, et toutes ces bonnes choses aussi.
La poupée merveilleuse, et le cheval de bois,
Et le mouton, sont là, dans ce coin tous les trois.
Et nous dormons, mais toutes ces bonnes choses sont à nous !
Les rideaux sont tirés... Là-bas, on ne sait où,
Dans la neige et la nuit sonne une espèce d'heure.
L'enfant dans son lit chaud comprend avec bonheur
Qu'il dort et que quelqu'un qui l'aime bien est là,
S'agite un peu, murmure vaguement, sort le bras,
Essaye de se réveiller et ne peut pas.

Only the gentle murmur of a kettle filled
Boils softly through the night. Between the beds,
On a shelf before the open hearth, which sheds
A drowsy light about Him where He reigns alone,
The Child Jesus of Prague sits on His throne.
Under a crystal globe, His crown upon His Head,
Holding the world in one hand, the other spread
To shelter all the little ones who trust in Him.
He looks lovable and sweet under the brim
Of that wide aureole, which like a yellow hat
Spreads out above His Head, magnificent and flat.
And underneath the weight of that long solemn dress,
He seems wistful and small. The shadows press
About Him from the dark, and like the Host withdrawn
The Christ Child guards His brothers till the dawn.
As softly as a gentle sigh across the gloom
His Holy Presence fills the corners of the room,
Enveloping the humble things within it, till
They too become eternal, magical, and still.
When He is here, our brother Jesus, then no harm
Can come to us, we sleep protected safe and warm.
For as these simple things we love belong to us
He too belongs to us; just as the marvelous
Great doll, the wooden horse, the woolly sheep,
Who all sit quiet in their corner while we sleep
Knowing that they are there. Far distant in the night,
Beyond the close-drawn curtains, and across the white
Wide space of snow, somewhere an hour strikes. The sound
Does not disturb the child buried in sleep profound,
Happy in his warm bed, smiling as if he feels
Someone who loves him well is here. Softly he steals
An arm out of the covers, moves a little, sighs
Vaguely, but cannot wake no matter how he tries.

(*Katherine Garrison Chapin*)

Paul Valéry

1871–1945

. .

LES GRENADES

DURES grenades entr'ouvertes
Cédant à l'excès de vos grains,
Je crois voir des fronts souverains
Eclatés de leurs découvertes!

Si les soleils pour vous subis,
O grenades entrebâillées,
Vous ont fait d'orgueil travaillées
Craquer les cloisons de rubis,

Et que si l'or sec de l'écorce
A la demande d'une force
Crève en gemmes rouges de jus,

Cette lumineuse rupture
Fait rêver une âme que j'eus
De sa secrète architecture.

HÉLÈNE

AZUR! c'est moi... Je viens des grottes de la mort
Entendre l'onde se rompre aux degrés sonores,
Et je revois les galères dans les aurores
Ressusciter de l'ombre au fil des rames d'or.

Paul Valéry

. .

POMEGRANATES

POMEGRANATES, fruit whose hard
Rind to rioting seed must yield—
One would think that he beheld
The sundered forehead of a god!

If the heat that you have borne,
O pomegranates opened wide,
Has, with the irritant of pride,
Made you crack your ruby walls,

And if your desiccate, golden shell,
From pressure of some hidden force,
Breaks in brilliant gems of juice,

I, at this luminous rupture, turn
My dry thought inward and discern
The architecture of the soul.

(William Jay Smith)

HELEN

O LIGHT, 'tis I, who from death's other shores
Have come to hear the cold wave climb the stone,
And see again a thousand ships at dawn
Emerge from dark to the beat of golden oars.

Mes solitaires mains appellent les monarques
Dont la barbe de sel amusait mes doigts purs;
Je pleurais. Ils chantaient leurs triomphes obscurs
Et les golfes enfuis des poupes de leurs barques,

J'entends les conques profondes et les clairons
Militaires rythmer le vol des avirons;
Le chant clair des rameurs enchaîne le tumulte,

Et les Dieux, à la proue héroïque exaltés
Dans leur sourire antique et que l'écume insulte
Tendent vers moi leurs bras indulgents et sculptés.

LE VIN PERDU

J'AI, quelque jour, dans l'Océan,
(Mais je ne sais plus sous quels cieux)
Jeté, comme offrande au néant,
Tout un peu de vin précieux...

Qui voulut ta perte, ô liqueur?
J'obéis peut-être au devin?
Peut-être au souci de mon coeur,
Songeant au sang, versant le vin?

Sa transparence accoutumée
Après un rose fumée
Reprit aussi pure la mer...

Perdu ce vin, ivres les ondes!...
J'ai vu bondir dans l'air amer
Les figures les plus profondes...

And now these lonely arms call back from night
The kings whose salty beards amused my hands.
I wept; they sang of dim and conquered lands,
And the gulf their beakèd vessels put to flight.

The echoing conch I hear and the trumpet call
Answer the rhythmic blade in its rise and fall,
The slaves' clear song that holds the sea in chains.

And watch the gods, exalted at the prow,
With a classic smile the bitter salt wave stains,
Extend their sculptured arms, forgiving all.

(*William Jay Smith*)

THE LOST WINE

ONE DAY into the sea I cast
(But where I cannot now divine)
As offering to oblivion,
My small store of precious wine . . .

What, oh rare liquor, willed your loss?
Some oracle half-understood?
Some hidden impulse of the heart
That made the poured wine seem like blood?

From this infusion of smoky rose
The sea regained its purity,
Its usual transparency . . .

Lost was the wine, and drunk the waves!
I saw high in the briny air
Forms unfathomed leaping there.

(*Barbara Howes*)

Alfred Jarry

1873–1907

· ·

FABLE

Une boîte de corned-beef, enchaînée comme une lorgnette,
Vit passer un homard qui lui ressemblait fraternellement.
Il se cuirassait d'une carapace dure
Sur laquelle était écrit qu'à l'intérieur, comme elle, il était sans
    arêtes,
(*Boneless and economical*)
Et sous sa queue repliée
Il cachait vraisemblablement une clé destinée à l'ouvrir.
Frappé d'amour, le corned-beef sédentaire
Déclara à la petite boîte automobile de conserves vivantes
Que si elle consentait à s'acclimater
Près de lui, aux devantures terrestres,
Elle serait décorée de plusieurs médailles d'or.

Alfred Jarry

. .

FABLE

A TIN of corned beef, chained like a lorgnette,
Saw a lobster go by, bearing a family resemblance to him.
He was buckled within a hard case
On which was written that inside, like her, he was boneless
(Boneless and economical)
And beneath his folded tail,
He probably hid a key for opening her.
Lovestricken, the sedentary corned beef
Declared to the little automobile box of living preserves
That if she'd deign to acclimatize herself
Staying by his side, in the terrestrial shopfront,
She too would be decorated with many gold medals.

(A. L. Lloyd)

Max Jacob

1876–1944

· ·

PETIT POÈME

Je me souviens de ma chambre d'enfant. La mousseline des rideaux sur la vitre était griffonnée de passementeries blanches, je m'efforçais d'y retrouver l'alphabet et quand je tenais les lettres, je les transformais en dessins que j'imaginais. H, un homme assis ; B, l'arche d'un pont sur un fleuve. Il y avait dans la chambre plusieurs coffres et des fleurs ouvertes sculptées légèrement sur le bois. Mais ce que je préférais, c'était deux boules de pilastres qu'on apercevait derrière les rideaux et que je considérais comme des têtes de pantins avec lesquels il était défendu de jouer.

Léon-Paul Fargue

1876–1947

· ·

MERDRIGAL

En dédicrasse

DANS mon cœur en ta présence
Fleurissent des harengs saurs.
Ma santé, c'est ton absence,
Et quand tu parais, je sors.

Max Jacob

. .

LITTLE POEM

I remember the room I had as a child. The muslin of the curtains at the window was trimmed with scrawling patterns, in which I endeavored to locate the alphabet and when I made out the letters, I transformed them into imaginary pictures. H was a man sitting, B, the arch of a bridge over a river. There were several chests in the room with open flowers delicately carved on their wood. But what I liked best were two knobs on the pillars you could see through the curtains, knobs that I took to be the heads of puppets with which it was forbidden to play.

(*William Jay Smith*)

Léon-Paul Fargue

. .

MUDDY MADRIGAL
Dedicrudory stanza

WITHIN my heart when you are here
Bunches of pickled herring bloom.
You go, I thrive; you reappear,
I sour quickly and leave the room.

(*William Jay Smith*)

Guillaume Apollinaire

1880–1918

. .

LA SAUTERELLE

Voici la fine sauterelle,
La nourriture de Saint Jean.
Puissent mes vers être comme elle,
Le régal des meilleures gens.

L'ÉCREVISSE

Incertitude, ô mes délices
Vous et moi nous nous en allons
Comme s'en vont les écrevisses,
A reculons, à reculons.

LA CARPE

Dans vos viviers, dans vos étangs,
Carpes, que vous vivez longtemps!
Est-ce que la mort vous oublie,
Poissons de la mélancolie.

LES SIRÈNES

Saché-je d'où provient, Sirènes, votre ennui
Quand vous vous lamentez, au large, dans la nuit?
Mer, je suis comme toi, plein de voix machinées
Et mes vaisseaux chantants se nomment les années.

Guillaume Apollinaire

. .

GRASSHOPPER

HERE IS the delicate grasshopper,
The diet of Saint John.
Be like her, my verses,
What the best folk nibble on.

CRAWFISH

INCERTITUDE, my secret joy,
To travel you and I
Must do as does the craw,
Withdraw, withdraw.

CARP

PLUNGED in wooded pools,
Carp, how old you live to be!
Have you slipped Death's mind,
Fishes of despond.

SIRENS

MAY I not know, Sirens, what stirs your discontent
When to the night you publish your lament?
Sea, I'm like you, machined cries fill my ears
And my vessels sing—they call themselves the years.

(*X. J. Kennedy*)

LE CHAT

JE SOUHAITE dans ma maison:
Une femme ayant sa raison,
Un chat passant parmi les livres,
Des amis en toute saison
Sans lesquels je ne peux pas vivre.

ANNIE

SUR la côte du Texas
Entre Mobile et Galveston il y a
Un grand jardin tout plein de roses
Il contient aussi une villa
Qui est une grande rose

Une femme se promène souvent
Dans le jardin toute seule
Et quand je passe sur la route bordée de tilleuls
Nous nous regardons

Comme cette femme est mennonite
Ses rosiers et ses vêtements n'ont pas de boutons
Il en manque deux à mon veston
La dame et moi suivons presque le même rite

THE CAT

I WANT in my own home:
A wife of sound reason
A cat among the books
Friends in every season
Without which I cannot live.

(*Roger Shattuck*)

ANNIE

BETWEEN Mobile and Galveston
On the seacoast of Texas
There's a big garden full of rosebushes
And a house like a big rose

Often there is a woman
Walking alone in the garden
And when I pass along the lime-bordered highway
We look at one another

She is a Mennonite this woman
And her rosebushes and clothes are buttonless
I see that two buttons are missing from my jacket
The lady and I observe almost the same rite

(*William Meredith*)

LES SAPINS

Les sapins en bonnets pointus
De longues robes revêtus
     Comme des astrologues
Saluent leurs frères abattus
Les bateaux qui sur le Rhin voguent

Dans les sept arts endoctrinés
Par les vieux sapins leurs aînés
     Qui sont de grands poètes
Ils se savent prédestinés
A briller plus que des planètes

A briller doucement changés
En étoiles et enneigés
     Aux Noëls bienheureuses
Fêtes des sapins ensongés
Aux longues branches langoureuses

Les sapins beaux musiciens
Chantent des noëls anciens
     Au vent des soirs d'automne
Ou bien graves magiciens
Incantent le ciel quand il tonne

Des rangées de blancs chérubins
Remplacent l'hiver les sapins
     Et balancent leurs ailes
L'été ce sont de grands rabbins
Ou bien de vieilles demoiselles

LES SAPINS

THE FIRS have pointed caps to wear
And skirted to the ground they stare
    Like astrologers
Over the river where ships steer,
    Fallen friends of theirs.

Seven arts with their degrees
They take from senior fellow trees,
    Great forest bards:
They know their destiny will blaze
    Brighter than stars.

The metamorphosis of firs
To snow-and-star-filled chandeliers
    On Christmas morning
Keeps their branches all astir
    With hopes and dreaming.

These firs are tuneable of voice
And sing the Christmas of old days
    To autumn airs,
Or chant like Druids to the skies
    When thunder roars.

White-winged cherubim in choirs
Alter the habits of the firs
    At fall of winter:
In summer, rabbis deep in beards
    Or antique spinsters.

Sapins médecins divagants
Ils vont offrant leurs bons onguents
Quand la montagne accouche
De temps en temps sous l'ouragan
Un vieux sapin geint et se couche

SALTIMBANQUES

À Louis Dumur

DANS la plaine des baladins
S'éloignent au long des jardins
Devant l'huis des auberges grises
Par les villages sans églises

Et les enfants s'en vont devant
Les autres suivent en rêvant
Chaque arbre fruitier se résigne
Quand de très loin ils lui font signe

Ils ont des poids ronds ou carrés
Des tambours des cerceaux dorés
L'ours et le singe animaux sages
Quêtent des sous sur leur passage

Like doctors feeble in the head
The firs believe their unguents good
    When the mountain labors:
Sometimes an old one cries aloud
Under a gale and falls down dead
    Beside his neighbors.

(*Louis O. Coxe*)

MOUNTEBANKS

THE MOUNTEBANKS appear like smoke
And through the churchless village walk
Passing the door of the gray inn
And off like smoke across the plain.

The children run in front and mime
Their elders follow in a dream
Fruit trees resign themselves to pillage
Once this music wakes the village.

They carry odd-shaped weights and props
And noisy drums and gilded hoops
And beasts with cups interpret where
They pass, a monkey and a bear.

(*William Meredith*)

Valery Larbaud

1881–1957

. .

SCHEVENINGUE, MORTE-SAISON

Dans le clair petit bar aux meubles bien cirés,
Nous avons longuement bu des boissons anglaises;
C'était intime et chaud sous les rideaux tirés.
Dehors le vent de mer faisait trembler les chaises.

On eût dit un fumoir de navire ou de train:
J'avais le cœur serré comme quand on voyage;
J'étais tout attendri, j'étais doux et lointain;
J'étais comme un enfant plein d'angoisse et très sage.

Cependant, tout était si calme autour de nous!
Des gens, près du comptoir, faisaient des confidences.
Oh, comme on est petit, comme on est à genoux,
Certains soirs, vous sentant si près, ô flots immenses!

Valery Larbaud

. .

SCHEVENINGEN, OFF SEASON

In a bright little bar that was carefully waxed,
Cozy and warm behind the drawn blinds,
Over long English drinks we sat and relaxed
While a sea wind rattled the chairs outside.

A wardroom it was or a Pullman clubcar:
And I felt as tense as one does en route;
I was very much moved, I was gentle and far,
Like a well-mannered child with a lump in his throat.

But everything there was completely at ease!
At the bar they spoke so we couldn't hear.
How small one feels, how down on one's knees,
On nights like this with the breakers near!

(*William Jay Smith*)

THALASSA

COUCHÉ sur le divan au fond de la cabine
(Bercé comme une poupée aux bras d'une fillette folle
Par le tangage et le roulis,—gros temps),
J'ai sur l'âme un cercle lumineux: le hublot,
Comme une vitrine de boutique où l'on vendrait la mer;
Et, à demi sommeillant, je rêve
De construire, dans une forme inusitée encore, un poème
A la gloire de la mer.

O Homère! ô Virgile!
O Corpus Poeticum Boreale! C'est dans vos pages
Qu'il faut chercher les vérités éternelles
De la mer, et ces mythes qui expriment un aspect du temps,
Et les féeries de la mer, et l'histoire des vagues,
Et le printemps marin, et l'automne marin,
Et l'accalmie qui fait une route plate et verte
Au char de Neptune et aux cortèges des Néréides.

J'ai sur l'âme un cercle lumineux qui voyage
De haut en bas, tantôt empli du bleu-gris moucheté de blanc
Du paysage méditerranéen, avec un coin de ciel
Pâle, tantôt
C'est le ciel qui descend remplir le cercle, tantôt
Je plonge dans une lumière glauque et froide,
Tourbillonnante, et tantôt, d'un seul coup,
Le hublot aveuglé de bave bondit s'éblouir en plein ciel blanc.

Passe, sur cette ligne d'horizon toujours mouvante,
Grand comme un jouet, un vapeur roumain, peint en blanc;
Il roule comme sur un chemin crevé de fondrières, et l'hélice
Sort parfois de la mer et bat l'air plein d'écume.
Ils saluent, du drapeau d'arrière, à mi-mât,
Bleu—jaune—rouge.

THALASSA

SEATED on a couch at the rear of my cabin
And rocked like a doll in the arms of some mad girl
By the pitch and roll of the ship in rough weather,
I bear upon my soul this luminous circle—this porthole
Which might be a shopwindow where one offered up the sea;
And, in my somnolent state, dream
Of constructing, in a form as yet untried, a poem
To the glory of the sea.

O Homer! O Virgil!
O Corpus Poeticum Boreale! It is in your pages
That one must look for the eternal verities
Of the sea, for those myths expressing an aspect of time,
The fairylands of the ocean, the history of the waves,
Marine spring, and marine autumn,
And the lull preparing a flat, green path
For Neptune and his procession of Nereids.

I bear upon my soul this luminous circle as it travels
Up and down, now filled with the white-speckled, blue-gray
Mediterranean landscape, and a corner of pale
Sky, and now
The sky descends into the circle, and now
I sink into a glaucous, cold,
Whirling light, and now of a sudden
The porthole, blinded by foam, wheels dazzled into the clear sky.

On the constantly shifting line of the horizon,
No bigger than a child's toy, a white Roumanian steamer
Passes,
Meeting the waves as if they were deep ruts in a road, the screw
Emerging from the water and whipping up the foam;
And signals to us, dipping its ensign,
Blue—yellow—red.

Bruits du navire: voix dans un corridor,
Craquements des boiseries, grincements des lampes oscillantes,
Rythme des machines, leur odeur fade par bouffées,
Cris mangés de vent, qui brouillent la musique
D'une mandoline égrenant: "Sobre las olas del mar..."
Et le bruit coutumier qui finit par être silence.

Oh! sur le pont, là-haut, le vent long et féroce, le vent-pirate
Sifflant dans les cordages, et faisant claquer comme un fouet
Le drapeau de bandes et d'étoiles aux trois couleurs...

Ship's noises: voices in passageways,
The creaking of the wood, the grating of the lamps,
The throbbing of the engines with their stale smell,
Cries swallowed by the wind, drowning the music
Of a mandolin which strums: *Sobre las olas del mar* . . .
The usual sound, the usual silence.

Oh, to think of the raging wind up there on deck, the pirate-wind
Which, as it whistles through the rigging, makes
Those stars and stripes of three colors
Crack like a whip! . . .

(*William Jay Smith*)

Jules Supervielle
1884–1960

· ·

DANS LA FORÊT SANS HEURES

Dans la forêt sans heures
On abat un grand arbre.
Un vide vertical
Tremble en forme de fût
Près du tronc étendu.

Cherchez, cherchez oiseaux,
La place de vos nids
Dans ce haut souvenir
Tant qu'il murmure encore.

Jules Supervielle

. .

In the primeval wood
A noble tree is felled.
Vertical emptiness,
A column, vibrates there
Close to the downed trunk.

Birds, seek on, seek on,
In this tall memorial,
For the haven of your nests
So long as its murmuring lasts.

(*Barbara Howes*)

St.-John Perse

1887–

. .

"QUAND VOUS AUREZ FINI DE ME COIFFER, J'AURAI FINI DE VOUS HAÏR"
(*Éloges*)

"Quand vous aurez fini de me coiffer, j'aurai fini de vous haïr."
L'enfant veut qu'on le peigne sur le pas de la porte.
"Ne tirez pas ainsi sur mes cheveux. C'est déjà bien assez qu'il
faille qu'on me touche. Quand vous m'aurez coiffé, je vous aurai
haïe."
Cependant la sagesse du jour prend forme d'un bel arbre
et l'arbre balancé
qui perd une pincée d'oiseaux,
aux lagunes du ciel écaille un vert si beau qu'il n'y a de plus
vert que la punaise d'eau.
"Ne tirez pas si loin sur mes cheveux..."

A PRÉSENT LAISSEZ-MOI, JE VAIS SEUL
(*Éloges*)

A présent laissez-moi, je vais seul.
Je sortirai, car j'ai affaire: un insecte m'attend pour traiter. Je
me fais joie
du gros œil à facettes: anguleux, imprévu, comme le fruit du
cyprès.
Ou bien j'ai une alliance avec les pierres veinées-bleu: et vous
me laissez également,
assis, dans l'amitié de mes genoux.

St.-John Perse

. .

"WHEN YOU STOP COMBING MY HAIR, I'LL STOP HATING YOU"
(From *Éloges*)

"WHEN you stop combing my hair, I'll stop hating you."
The child wants his hair combed on the doorstep.
"Don't pull like that. It's bad enough being touched. When you've finished my hair, I'll have hated you."
Meanwhile the wisdom of day takes the shape of a fine tree
and the swaying tree,
loosing a pinch of birds,
scales off in the lagoons of the sky a green so beautiful, there is nothing that is greener except the water-bug.
"Don't pull on my hair so far . . ."

(Louise Varèse)

AND NOW LET ME BE, I GO ALONE
(From *Éloges*)

AND NOW let me be, I go alone.
I shall go out, for I have something to do: an insect is waiting to treat with me. I delight in
his big, faceted eye: angular, unexpected, like the fruit of the cypress.
Or else I have an alliance with the blue-veined stones: and also you'll let me be,
sitting, in the friendship of my knees.

(Louise Varèse)

Jean Cocteau

1889–1963

. .

LE MIRLITON D'IRÈNE

Rosier

AFIN que leur fantaisie
Ne soit pas que du carton,
Rosier de la poésie,
Grimpe autour des mirlitons.

Fruit

Un lampion du dimanche,
S'il est mûri par le vent,
Peut mettre le feu aux branches;
Il faut le cueillir avant.

Chat

Le feu: jolis poissons rouges,
Endormait le chat fermé.
Si, par mégarde, je bouge,
Le chat peut se transformer.

Il ne faut jamais que cesse
Le rouet des vieilles tours;
Car se changer en princesse
Est le moindre de ses tours.

Jean Cocteau

. .

IRENE'S PENNYWHISTLE

Rose Tree

IN ORDER that their fantasies
may not be only cardboard poses,
around the airs of pennywhistles,
poetry, like roses.

Fruit

A Sunday lantern,
if ripened by the breeze,
may, unless it's picked in time,
set fire to all the trees.

Cat

By the fire, like drifting reddish goldfish,
the cat dozed, curled within itself.
If, by mischance, I were to stir,
the cat might change to something else.

The spinning-wheel of ancient magic
must never be allowed to stick:
and changing itself into a princess
is, for the cat, a minor trick.

Vésuve

Naples, ses tarentelles
Montrent son joli pied;
Mais la belle en dentelles
Fume comme un troupier.

Trouville

L'océan, comme émeraude.
A certes quelques défauts;
Mais la baigneuse nigaude
Aime mieux les bijoux faux.

Prise sur le fait

Jeu de cartes
ou éventail?

Elle triche.

Accordéon

Accordéon, cheval de fiacre,
Le dernier soupir arraché,
Tu meurs, en riant de la nacre,
Sur les genoux de ton cocher.

Minuit

L'enfant dort.
                    A Noël il fait semblant.
(Jeune mère cela vous met à l'aise.)
A côté veille, assis sur la chaise,
Son ange gardien, ramoneur blanc.

Vesuvius

In Naples, tarantellas
show many a pretty slipper;
the beautiful lady in lace, however,
is smoking like a trooper.

Trouville

There are certain patent flaws
in the emerald-like sea;
but the gawking bathing-girl
prefers her own false jewelry.

Caught in the Act

Hands of cards
or a fan?

She is cheating.

Accordion

Accordion, like a coach-horse,
wheezing your last sigh,
merry in mother-of-pearl,
on your coachman's knees, you die.

Midnight

The child is sleeping.
                    At Christmas he pretends.
(Let that put you at your ease, young mother.)
Watching by his side, in a chair, sitting
his guardian angel, a snow-white chimney sweep.

(*Alastair Reid*)

Paul Éluard

1895–1952

. .

LIBERTÉ

SUR MES cahiers d'écolier
Sur mon pupitre et les arbres
Sur le sable sur la neige
J'écris ton nom

Sur toutes les pages lues
Sur toutes les pages blanches
Pierre sang papier ou cendre
J'écris ton nom

Sur les images dorées
Sur les armes des guerriers
Sur la couronne des rois
J'écris ton nom

Sur la jungle et le désert
Sur les nids sur les genêts
Sur l'écho de mon enfance
J'écris ton nom

Sur les merveilles des nuits
Sur le pain blanc des journées
Sur les saisons fiancées
J'écris ton nom

Paul Éluard

.   .

LIBERTY

ON MY schoolboy's notebooks
On my desk and on the trees
On sand on snow
I write your name

On all pages read
On all blank pages
Stone blood paper or ash
I write your name

On gilded images
On the weapons of warriors
On the crowns of kings
I write your name

On jungle and desert
On nests on gorse
On the echo of my childhood
I write your name

On the wonders of nights
On the white bread of days
On betrothed seasons
I write your name

Sur tous mes chiffons d'azur
Sur l'étang soleil moisi
Sur le lac lune vivante
J'écris ton nom

Sur les champs sur l'horizon
Sur les ailes des oiseaux
Et sur le moulin des ombres
J'écris ton nom

Sur chaque bouffée d'aurore
Sur la mer sur les bateaux
Sur la montagne démente
J'écris ton nom

Sur la mousse des nuages
Sur les sueurs de l'orage
Sur la pluie épaisse et fade
J'écris ton nom

Sur les formes scintillantes
Sur les cloches des couleurs
Sur la vérité physique
J'écris ton nom

Sur les sentiers éveillés
Sur les routes déployées
Sur les places qui débordent
J'écris ton nom

Sur la lampe qui s'allume
Sur la lampe qui s'éteint
Sur mes maisons réunies
J'écris ton nom

On all my rags of azure
On the pool musty sun
On the lake living moon
I write your name

On fields on the horizon
On the wings of birds
And on the mill of shadows
I write your name

On each puff of dawn
On the sea on ships
On the demented mountain
I write your name

On the foam of clouds
On the sweat of storm
On thick insipid rain
I write your name

On shimmering shapes
On bells of color
On physical truth
I write your name

On awakened pathways
On roads spread out
On overflowing squares
I write your name

On the lamp that is lit
On the lamp that burns out
On my reunited houses
I write your name

Sur le fruit coupé en deux
Du miroir et de ma chambre
Sur mon lit coquille vide
J'écris ton nom

Sur mon chien gourmand et tendre
Sur ses oreilles dressées
Sur sa patte maladroite
J'écris ton nom

Sur le tremplin de ma porte
Sur les objets familiers
Sur le flot du feu béni
J'écris ton nom

Sur toute chair accordée
Sur le front de mes amis
Sur chaque main qui se tend
J'écris ton nom

Sur la vitre des surprises
Sur les lèvres attentives
Bien au-dessus du silence
J'écris ton nom

Sur mes refuges détruits
Sur mes phares écroulés
Sur les murs de mon ennui
J'écris ton nom

Sur l'absence sans désir
Sur la solitude nue
Sur les marches de la mort
J'écris ton nom

On the fruit cut in two
Of the mirror and my chamber
On my bed empty shell
I write your name

On my dog greedy and tender
On his trained ears
On his awkward paw
I write your name

On the springboard of my door
On familiar objects
On the flood of blessed fire
I write your name

On all tuned flesh
On the foreheads of my friends
On each hand outstretched
I write your name

On the window of surprises
On the attentive lips
Well above silence
I write your name

On my destroyed refuges
On my crumbled beacons
On the walls of my weariness
I write your name

On absence without desire
On naked solitude
On the steps of death
I write your name

Sur la santé revenue
Sur le risque disparu
Sur l'espoir sans souvenir
J'écris ton nom

Et par le pouvoir d'un mot
Je recommence ma vie
Je suis né pour te connaître
Pour te nommer

Liberté

On health returned
On the risk disappeared
On hope without memory
I write your name

And by the power of a word
I start my life again
I was born to know you
To name you

Liberty

(*Lloyd Alexander*)

Francis Ponge

1899–

. .

LA POMME DE TERRE

PELER une pomme de terre bouillie de bonne qualité est un plaisir de choix.

Entre le gras du pouce et la pointe du couteau tenu par les autres doigts de la même main, l'on saisit—après l'avoir incisé—par l'une de ses lèvres ce rêche et fin papier que l'on tire à soi pour le détacher de la chair appétissante du tubercule.

L'opération facile laisse, quand on a réussi à la parfaire sans s'y reprendre à trop de fois, une impression de satisfaction indicible.

Le léger bruit que font les tissus en se décollant est doux à l'oreille, et la découverte de la pulpe comestible réjouissante.

Il semble, à reconnaître la perfection du fruit nu, sa différence, sa ressemblance, sa surprise—et la facilité de l'opération—que l'on ait accompli là quelque chose de juste, dès longtemps prévu et souhaité par la nature, que l'on a eu toutefois le mérite d'exaucer.

C'est pourquoi je n'en dirai pas plus, au risque de sembler me satisfaire d'un ouvrage trop simple. Il ne me fallait—en quelques phrases sans effort—que déshabiller mon sujet, en en contournant strictement la forme: la laissant intacte mais polie, brillante et toute prête à subir comme à procurer les délices de sa consommation.

...Cet apprivoisement de la pomme de terre par son traitement à l'eau bouillante durant vingt minutes, c'est assez curieux (mais justement tandis que j'écris des pommes de terre cuisent—il est une heure du matin—sur le fourneau devant moi).

Il vaut mieux, m'a-t-on dit, que l'eau soit salée, sévère: pas obligatoire mais c'est mieux.

Francis Ponge

. .

THE POTATO

PEELING a high-quality boiled potato is an exquisite pleasure.

Between the fleshy cushion of the thumb and the blade of the knife held in the other fingers of the same hand, you clasp—after making an incision—one of the lips of this delicate, grainy paper, drawing it toward you, stripping it from the appetizing flesh of the tuber.

This simple operation, if carried out in a few smooth strokes, leaves you with a sense of indescribable satisfaction.

The faint sound made by the membranes as they are detached is delightful to hear, and the unveiling of the edible pulp a joyful discovery.

As you realize the perfection of the naked fruit: transformed, surprised and yet the same—as well as the ease of the operation—you feel that you have accomplished something precise, a task long anticipated and desired by nature, one which, nevertheless, you deserve a certain credit for fulfilling.

That is why I won't say anything more, for fear of seeming satisfied with too easy an achievement. All I had to do—in a few effortless sentences—was undress my subject, following its exact contours, leaving it intact but polished, shining, ready both to consummate and to be consumed.

. . . This taming of the potato by treating it in boiling water for twenty minutes is rather curious (just as I am writing, potatoes are cooking—it is one in the morning—on the stove before me).

The water, I was told, should be harsh and salted. This is not necessary, but preferable.

Une sorte de vacarme se fait entendre, celui des bouillons de l'eau. Elle est en colère, au moins au comble de l'inquiétude. Elle se déperd furieusement en vapeurs, bave, grille aussitôt, pfutte, tsitte: enfin, très agitée sur ces charbons ardents.

Mes pommes de terre, plongées là dedans, sont secouées de soubresauts, bousculées, injuriées, imprégnées jusqu'à la moelle.

Sans doute la colère de l'eau n'est-elle pas à leur propos, mais elles en supportent l'effet—et ne pouvant se déprendre de ce milieu, elles s'en trouvent profondément modifiées (j'allais écrire s'entrouvrent . . .).

Finalement, elles y sont laissées pour mortes, ou du moins très fatiguées. Si leur forme en réchappe (de qui n'est pas toujours), elles sont devenues molles, dociles. Toute acidité a disparu de leur pulpe: on leur trouve bon goût.

Leur épiderme s'est aussi rapidement différencié: il faut l'ôter (il n'est plus bon à rien), et le jeter aux ordures...

Reste ce bloc friable et savoureux,—qui prête moins qu'à d'abord vivre, ensuite à philosopher.

A kind of commotion arises from the turbulent water. It is furious, or at least seriously disturbed. It squanders itself in clouds of steam, foams over, sizzles: ssss, ssss, psst; beside itself, really, on the fiery coals.

My potatoes, submerged in all this, are shaken about, jolted, assaulted, impregnated to the pith.

The water's fury, most likely, has little to do with them, and yet they endure its effects; unable to escape the situation, they are left deeply altered (I was going to say cleft deeply . . .)

In the end they are left for dead. Worn out, anyway. Even if they have kept their figures (which is not always the case) they have become soft and malleable. All acidity has disappeared from the flesh; they now taste good.

The epidermis, too, has undergone a rapid change; now worthless, it must be removed and thrown in the garbage . . .

A crumbly, toothsome portion remains—one which enables you not merely to live, but to philosophize.

(Merloyd Lawrence)

Robert Desnos

1900–1945

. .

LE SOLEIL

Soleil en terre, tournesol,
Dis-moi qu'as-tu fait de la lune?

Elle est au ciel, moi sur le sol,
Mais nous avons même fortune
Car sur nous-mêmes nous tournons
Comme des fous au cabanon.

Robert Desnos

. .

SUN

SUN in the earth, sunflower,
What have you done with the moon?

She's in the sky, I'm on the ground,
　Yet our two fates are one
For round ourselves we go round
　Like madmen in a pound.

(*X. J. Kennedy*)

Jacques Prévert

1900–

. .

SABLES MOUVANTS

DÉMONS et merveilles
Vents et marées
Au loin déjà la mer s'est retirée
Et toi
Comme une algue doucement caressée par le vent
Dans les sables du lit tu remues en rêvant
Démons et merveilles
Vents et marées
Au loin déjà la mer s'est retirée
Mais dans tes yeux entr'ouverts
Deux petites vagues sont restées
Démons et merveilles
Vents et marées
Deux petites vagues pour me noyer.

LE RETOUR AU PAYS

C'EST un Breton qui revient au pays natal
Après avoir fait plusieurs mauvais coups
Il se promène devant les fabriques à Douarnenez
Il ne reconnaît personne
Personne ne le reconnaît
Il est très triste.

Jacques Prévert

. .

SABLES MOUVANTS

DEMONS and wonders
Winds and waters
Now the sea ebbs in far retreat
Like seaweed a tender seawind fondles
In the sand of the bed you sway in sleep
Demons and wonders
Winds and waters
Now the sea ebbs in far retreat
Yet in your eyes, half-open
Two small swells keep
Demons and wonders
Winds and waters
Two small swells to drown me deep.

(*Louis O. Coxe*)

HOMECOMING

A BRETON returns to his birthplace
After having pulled off several fast deals
He walks in front of the factories at Douarnenez
He recognizes nobody
Nobody recognizes him
He is very sad

Il entre dans une crêperie pour manger des crêpes
Mais il ne peut pas en manger
Il a quelque chose qui les empêche de passer
Il paye
Il sort
Il allume une cigarette
Mais il ne peut pas la fumer.
Il y a quelque chose
Quelque chose dans sa tête
Quelque chose de mauvais
Il est de plus en plus triste
Et soudain il se met à se souvenir :
Quelqu'un lui a dit quand il était petit
"Tu finiras sur l'échafaud"
Et pendant des années
Il n'a jamais osé rien faire
Pas même traverser la rue
Pas même partir sur la mer
Rien absolument rien.
Il se souvient.
Celui qui avait tout prédit c'est l'oncle Grésillard
L'oncle Grésillard qui portait malheur à tout le monde
La vache
Et le Breton pense à sa sœur
Qui travaille à Vaugirard
À son frère mort à la guerre
Pense à toutes les choses qu'il a vues
Toutes les choses qu'il a faites.
La tristesse se serre contre lui
Il essaie une nouvelle fois
D'allumer une cigarette
Mais il n'a pas envie de fumer
Alors il décide d'aller voir l'oncle Grésillard.
Il y va

He goes into a *crêpe* shop to eat some *crêpes*
But he can't eat any
There's something that keeps him from swallowing
He pays
He goes out
He lights a cigarette
But he can't smoke it
There's something
Something in his head
Something bad
He gets sadder and sadder
And suddenly he begins to remember:
Somebody told him when he was little
"You'll end up on the scaffold"
And for years
He never dared do anything
Not even cross the street
Not even go to sea
Nothing absolutely nothing.
He remembers.
The one who'd predicted everything was Uncle Grésillard
Uncle Grésillard who brought everybody bad luck
The swine!
And the Breton thinks of his sister
Who works at Vaugirard,
Of his brother killed in the War
Thinks of all the things he's seen
All the things he's done.
Sadness grips him
He tries again
To light a cigarette
But he doesn't feel like smoking
So then he decides to go see Uncle Grésillard.
He goes.

Il ouvre la porte
L'oncle ne le reconnaît pas
Mais lui le reconnaît
Et il lui dit:
"Bonjour oncle Grésillard"
Et puis il lui tord le cou.
Et il finit sur l'échafaud à Quimper
Après avoir mangé deux douzaines de crêpes
Et fumé une cigarette.

He opens the door
Uncle doesn't recognize him
But he recognizes him
And he says to him
"Good morning Uncle Grésillard"
And then he wrings his neck
And he ends up on the scaffold at Quimper
After having eaten two dozen *crêpes*
And smoked a cigarette.

(*Lawrence Ferlinghetti*)

IMMENSE ET ROUGE

Immense et rouge
Au-dessus du Grand Palais
Le soleil d'hiver apparaît
Et disparaît
Comme lui mon cœur va disparaître
Et tout mon sang va s'en aller
S'en aller à ta recherche
Mon amour
Ma beauté
Et te trouver
Là où tu es.

IMMENSE AND RED

Immense and red
Above the Grand Palais appears
The sun in winter
And then disappears
My heart like that sun will also disappear
Like it my blood will all drain away
Will go in search of you
Beauty
My love
And find you one day
There where you stay.

(*William Jay Smith*)

Biographies of the Poets

GUILLAUME APOLLINAIRE (1880–1918) was born Wilhelm Apollinaris de Kostrowitsky in Rome. The friend of Picasso and Braque, he wrote the manifesto of Cubist painting. His poetic reputation was established by *Alcools* (1913) and strengthened by *Calligrammes* (1918), which he wrote in the trenches in World War I and in which he experimented with pictorial typography. He died of wounds received in the war. His poetry, in its freshness and lyric vigor, has been an important influence in the twentieth century.

THÉODORE de BANVILLE (1823–1891), one of the greatest poetic technicians and masters of light verse, known for his revival of Old French verse forms. *Les Cariatides* (1842), *Les Stalactites* (1846), and *Les Odes funambulesques* (1857) show his delightful, witty range. His *Petit Traité de la poésie française* (1872) is one of the best studies of the art of versification.

CHARLES BAUDELAIRE (1821–1867). In 1841 his stepfather, Colonel Aupick, whom he detested, sent him off on a journey to India to cure him of his bohemian habits, but Baudelaire returned after reaching the island of Mauritius and embarked on a literary career. He began by translating works of Edgar Allan Poe. His great work, *Les Fleurs du mal* (1857), in which he examines in carefully composed classical stanzas the nature of hypersensitive modern man, is his masterpiece. With his keen analysis of complex psychological states and the introduction of the imagery of urban life, he has been an important influence on modern poetry. His prose poems in *Le Spleen de Paris*, published after his death, are filled with striking imagery; he was a brilliant critic of music and painting.

ANDRÉ CHÉNIER (1762–1794) is generally considered the greatest poet of the eighteenth century. While classical in spirit, he was important for his metrical innovations which anticipated those of the romantics. He sympathized at first with the Revolution, but was later horrified by its excesses, and was guillotined after his attacks on Robespierre.

PAUL CLAUDEL (1868–1955), poet, dramatist, and diplomat, was converted to Roman Catholicism in 1886; his poetry and plays express his deep faith. He served as a diplomat for many years in China, and later as ambassador to the United States. His poems, written in unrhymed *versets*, often have a Biblical sweep.

JEAN COCTEAU (1889–1963) was one of the leaders of every literary and artistic movement between the two world wars. His work includes poetry, essays, novels, plays, ballets, and films, all of which reflect the wide range of his imagination and his keen intelligence. His chief collections of poetry are *Poésies 1916–23* (1924), *Opéra 1925–1927* (1927), and *Poésies* (1947).

TRISTAN CORBIÈRE (1845–1875), the son of a writer of sea stories, was unable because of poor health to realize his ambition to become a sailor, but in hard-bitten, ironic lines he captured much of the life of the sea and of his native coast of Brittany in the poems of *Les Amours jaunes* (1873), which became an important influence on modern poetry.

CHARLES CROS (1842–1888), besides being the author of the many witty and delicate poems assembled in two principal collections, *Le Coffret de santal* (1873) and *Le Collier de griffes* (1908), was also a pioneer in color photography and an inventor credited with a version of the phonograph that preceded Edison's.

MARCELINE DESBORDES-VALMORE (1786–1859), was brought up in poverty, went on the stage, married an actor, and for twenty years toured the country with him. In her lyrics, concerned principally with love and childhood, she refers frequently to an unhappy love affair. Verlaine included her poems in his *Poètes Maudits* in 1884.

EUSTACHE DESCHAMPS (1346?–?1406) held various court positions under Charles V. He was the author of many poems on a variety of subjects, among them the long unfinished *Miroir de mariage*, which is a satire on women. He also wrote in prose *Art de dicter et de faire chansons*, which is the oldest work of French poetic theory.

ROBERT DESNOS (1900–1945) started his career as a surrealist poet. His first important work was *Deuil pour deuil* (1924). He later turned to writing simple, straightforward lyrics. A journalist and script writer for radio, he was active in the French Resistance, and was imprisoned in concentration camps in Germany. He died at Terezin in Czechoslovakia. His volume *Corps et Biens* (1930) contains poems written between 1919 and 1930. He also wrote a charming collection of children's poems, *30 Chantefables pour les enfants sages* (1944).

JOACHIM DU BELLAY (1522–1560) was, with Ronsard, one of the founders of La Pléiade. In 1549 he published his *Défense et illustration de la langue française*, which was the manifesto of the school. One of its chief tenets was the creation of new words. He accompanied his uncle, a cardinal, to Rome, where he wrote some of his most famous poems. He was a master of the sonnet form, and many of his sonnets were translated by Edmund Spenser.

PAUL ÉLUARD, pen name of Eugéne Grindel (1895–1952), was, with André Breton, one of the founders of surrealism. He later became an eloquent spokesman for love and liberty. The early poems collected in *Capitale de la douleur* (1926) are among his best. *Poèmes politiques* (1948) are typical of his later work, which takes the form of direct and passionate statement and is less concerned with the nuance between dream and reality.

LÉON-PAUL FARGUE (1876–1947) shows in his *Poèmes* (1912) the wit, verbal invention, and lyric ease which made him the poet *par excellence* of modern city life. He is especially remembered for his memoirs of life in his native city, *Le Piéton de Paris* (1939).

THÉOPHILE GAUTIER (1811–1872) first studied painting, and his love of visual and plastic qualities is apparent in all his work. In a scarlet doublet, he led the claque of supporters on the famous opening night of Hugo's drama *Hernani* (1830). In the preface to his novel *Mademoiselle de Maupin* (1835) he set forth his doctrine of Art for Art's sake. This doctrine is beautifully elucidated in the exquisite, chiseled verses of *Émaux et camées* (1852), on which his poetic reputation is based.

JOSÉ MARIA de HEREDIA (1842–1905), born in Cuba of a Cuban father and a French mother, was educated in France. Perhaps the finest of the Parnassian poets, he published only one volume of poems, *Les Trophées* (1893), a collection of 118 sonnets, some of them among the finest in French literature.

VICTOR HUGO (1802–1885), whose work covers almost an entire century, was the greatest poet of his time, and, in the opinion of some, of all French literature. His career as a writer—as a novelist and dramatist as well as a poet—was varied and its range phenomenal. Although one of the leading romantic figures, he transcends his period, and in poetry, personal and reflective, and at times of epic sweep, sounds the organ note of French poetic genius. In volumes like *Les Feuilles d'Automne* (1831) and *La Légende des siècles* (1859–1883) and the unfinished *La Fin de Satan* (1886) he is at his lyrical best; and in *Les Châtiments* (1853) he writes poetry inspired by a public and prophetic view of the poet's role. The poems in the latter volume were an attack on the government of Napoleon III, whose rise to power was responsible for Hugo's exile to the Channel Islands. After the fall of the Second Empire, he returned to France and was elected a deputy. He was buried in Paris in 1885 with all the pomp and glory of a national hero.

MAX JACOB (1876–1944), Cubist poet and friend of Apollinaire, came to Paris from Brittany. He was converted to Roman Catholicism in 1914, and after 1921, settled at Saint-Benoît-sur-Loire; he died in a German concentration camp at Drancy during World War II. The early prose poems collected in *Le Cornet à dés* (1918) are among his most famous.

FRANCIS JAMMES (1868–1938). His poems, characterized by a simplicity of feeling, deal almost entirely with rustic life. *De l'angélus à l'aube à l'angélus du soir* (1898) contains his most representative work. After his conversion to Roman Catholicism in 1905, his work became more religious in inspiration.

ALFRED JARRY (1873–1907) is best known for his farce *Ubu Roi* (1896), whose principal character "Le Père Ubu" is the grotesque embodiment of bourgeois stupidity, and for his novel *Le Surmâle* (1902). His special humor, which stresses the power of hallucination, makes him an important precursor of surrealism.

LOUISE LABÉ (c. 1524–1566), the wife of a wealthy ropemaker of Lyon, was sometimes referred to as *la belle cordière*. The lyrics and sonnets in her *Oeuvres* (1555) have in their passionate intensity been compared to those of Sappho.

JEAN de LA FONTAINE (1621–1695), a prolific writer, spent most of his life in idleness, dependent on one patron after another. His fame rests on his *Fables*, the first collection of which appeared in 1668. The fables, written in a direct and easy style, have been translated many times into English, most recently by Marianne Moore.

JULES LAFORGUE (1860–1887), born at Montevideo, was for five years (1881–1886) reader to the Empress Augusta in Berlin. He was one of the first to use *vers libre*, and his ironical detachment and use of colloquial language were imitated by twentieth-century American and English poets. His most important works are *Les Complaintes* (1885), *L'Imitation de Notre-Dame la Lune* (1886), and *Derniers Vers* (1886–1887). In his *Moralités légendaires* (1887), published posthumously, he treats myths and legends in a light and mocking fashion. He wrote one of the earliest, and still the best, essays on impressionist painting.

ALPHONSE de LAMARTINE (1790–1869), one of the leaders of the romantic movement, was a statesman as well as a poet. A liberal in politics, he achieved prominence during the revolution of 1848 but soon fell from power. His *Méditations poétiques* (1820), which included the famous poem *Le Lac*, brought him immediate fame. In his melodious verses he presents Nature as a reflection of his own moods.

VALERY LARBAUD (1881–1957), born at Vichy, traveled widely in his youth, and published his *Poèmes par un riche amateur* in 1908. These poems were purported to be the work of A. O. Barnabooth, a wealthy South American millionaire. While superficially dealing only with exotic landscape, they expressed a lyrical longing for an indefinable absolute. They were collected together with the *Journal d'A. O. Barnabooth* (1918). Larbaud was also a novelist and man of letters. Widely read in English literature, he was a friend of James Joyce, and one of the first critics to help launch *Ulysses* (1922).

LECONTE de LISLE (1818–1894), born on Réunion Island, came to Paris to study law, but soon turned to the translation of Greek classics. Out of his love of Greek poetry grew his own objective lyricism, which made him the recognized leader of the Parnassian school of poets. His *Poèmes antiques* appeared in 1852, and his *Poèmes barbares* in 1862.

STÉPHANE MALLARMÉ (1842–1898) formulated the aesthetic theories of the symbolist school. He earned his living by teaching English, first in the provinces and then in Paris, where from 1885 to 1894 poets gathered on Tuesdays in his flat in the rue de Rome. His difficult poems, which he wrote slowly and with great concentration, are notable for their resonance and power of suggestion. His best-known works are *L'Après-midi d'un faune* (1876), which inspired the Prelude of Debussy, *Les Poésies* (1887), and *Divagations* (1897).

CLÉMENT MAROT (1496–1544), whose varied, graceful, and witty lyrics form a link between medieval poetry and the poetry of the Renaissance, was much admired by the classic poets of the seventeenth century. He was one of the first poets to adopt the Italian sonnet into French. His translation from Latin of the Psalms (1541–1543) reflects his interest in Calvinism.

JEAN MORÉAS, pen name of Yannis Pappadiamantopoulos (1856–1910). Born in Athens of Greek parentage, he became, with Charles Maurras and Ernest Raynaud, the founder of the École Romane; his best poems, notable for their classical restraint, appear in *Les Stances* (1899–1901).

ALFRED de MUSSET (1810–1857) was one of the great figures of the romantic movement, particularly noted for the music of his poetry and the graceful lyricism of his plays, which were comedies of manners called *comédies-proverbes*. His disastrous affair with George Sand is described in an autobiographical novel *Confession d'un enfant du siècle* (1836).

GÉRARD de NERVAL (1808–1855), whose real name was Gérard Labrunie, had in 1841 his first attack of madness. His poetry, which reaches its height in the sonnets of *Les Chimères* (1854) is a kind of incantation to a lost and invisible world. He is an important precursor of Baudelaire and the surrealists. Although the material of his poems and stories (the most famous of which is *Sylvie*) is often hallucinatory, their style is always lucid. He hanged himself at the age of forty-seven in the rue de la Vieille Lanterne in the old quarter of Paris.

CHARLES d'ORLÉANS (1391–1465) was taken prisoner at Agincourt, and spent twenty-five years in exile in England. In his later years at Blois, he surrounded himself with poets and brought his poetry to perfection.

ST.-JOHN PERSE, pen name of Alexis Saint-Léger Léger (1887–   ), poet and diplomat, was born on a family-owned island near Guadeloupe. He came to France to study, gave up medicine to enter the diplomatic service. Léger served for years in China and became a specialist in the Far East. He fled from France in 1940 after the Vichy government had confiscated his possessions, returned from the United States in 1959, and was awarded the Nobel Prize for Literature in 1960. His early works were *Éloges* (1911) and *Amitié du Prince* (1924). He later published *Pluies* (1943), *Neiges* (1944), *Vents* (1946), and *Chronique* (1960), all of which present a vast panorama of history and praise the poet as creator. His style shows the influence of Claudel, and, like Claudel's, his are poems of praise—but praise of man rather than God.

CHRISTINE de PISAN (1364–?1431) was born in Venice, the daughter of an Italian physician in the service of Charles V. She was left a widow at twenty-five, and wrote to help support her three children. Her ballades and rondeaux are chiefly concerned with love. She wrote also numerous prose works, among them notably *Livres de faits et bonnes moeurs du sage roi Charles V* (1404).

FRANCIS PONGE (1899–   ) writes prose poems in which objects take on a life of their own. His philosophical attempt to express objective reality is shown in his volume *Le Parti pris des choses* (1942). His work since World War II has been an important influence on young poets and novelists.

JACQUES PRÉVERT (1900–   ) began as a member of the sur-realist group, but since World War II has become famous for his songs and film scripts. The poems in *Paroles* (1960) are often satirical and mock-ing, but more often they praise the life of the senses. As the title of his book indicates, his poems are meant to be spoken, and his revival of the oral folk tradition in poetry has made his work widely popular.

MATHURIN RÉGNIER (1573–1613). His *Satires*, modeled on the satires of Horace and Juvenal and written in alexandrines, made him an important precursor of Molière.

ARTHUR RIMBAUD (1854–1891), one of the greatest prodigies in all literature, ran away from home at the age of fifteen, and steeping himself in occult writing, produced poems of great force and originality. After his brief and tumultuous liaison with Verlaine, he traveled about Europe, and finally, at the age of nineteen or twenty, abandoned literature and became a trader in what is now Ethiopia. *Les Illuminations* (1886) and *Une Saison en Enfer* (1872–1873) have been important influences on modern poetry in both French and English.

PIERRE de RONSARD (1524–1585), leader of the group of poets known as La Pléiade, began life as a page at the court of Francis I, but was prevented from undertaking a diplomatic career because of deafness. His great technical versatility and lyrical brilliance made him known throughout Europe as "the Prince of Poets." His work, however, was neglected after his death, and interest in it was not revived until the nine-teenth century.

EDMOND ROSTAND (1868–1918), poet and playwright, won fame with his poetic drama *Cyrano de Bergerac* (1897), from which the *Ballade* is taken. Sarah Bernhardt had great success in the title role of *L'Aiglon* (1900), an historical drama based on the life of Napoleon's son. His last play, *Chantecler* (1910), was a critical success but was poorly received.

JULES SUPERVIELLE (1884–1960), poet, novelist, and short-story writer, was born at Montevideo, and after schooling in France, resided permanently in Uruguay, until he returned to Paris after World War II. His poetry, which often reflects his familiarity with the South American scene, is noted for its purity of language and freshness of lyricism.

PAUL-JEAN TOULET (1867–1920), poet and novelist, was born at Pau; his parents were from Mauritius. He is best known for the elegant polished verses of *Contrerimes*, in which there is a subtle blend of irony, eroticism, and fantasy.

PAUL VALÉRY (1871–1945) was born at Sète on the Mediterranean of an Italian mother and a French father. He studied law at Montpellier, came to Paris in 1892, and frequented the salons of Mallarmé, who became a lasting influence on his work. His *Introduction à la méthode de Léonard de Vinci* (1895) explored the creative process. He continued to interest himself in abstract thought and wrote little until 1912 when he was persuaded by friends to collect his earlier poems in *Album de vers anciens* (1920), to which he added *La Jeune Parque* (1917). A further collection, *Charmes* (1922), established his reputation as one of the greatest twentieth-century poets.

PAUL VERLAINE (1844–1896), noted for the grace and delicacy of his lyric poetry, lived a life which alternated between debauchery and religious repentance. He abandoned his young wife in 1872 and left for England in the company of Rimbaud. Their liaison ended in Brussels when Verlaine shot at Rimbaud and wounded him in the wrist. Sentenced to two years in prison, he was converted to Roman Catholicism (his conversion is celebrated in the poems of *Sagesse* [1881]). The remainder of his life was marked by further periods of drunkenness and debauchery. *Fêtes galantes* (1869) and *Romances sans paroles* (1874) contain some of his best poems.

ALFRED de VIGNY (1797–1863), the son of an aristocratic family ruined by the Revolution, spent his early years in the army. He published in 1826 *Cinq-Mars*, a historical novel in the manner of Scott. Married to an English woman, he translated Shakespeare, and wrote one of the best romantic dramas, *Chatterton*, based on the life of the poet. His poetry reflects his spiritual loneliness and stoical despair; he is the most intellectual of the romantic poets.

FRANÇOIS VILLON (1431–?1489) was originally called François de Montcorbier or François de Loges. A brilliant student, he fell in early with bad company, was involved in several crimes, and had to flee Paris. Although he wrote little more than 3,000 lines, he is considered the finest poet of the Middle Ages. His famous *Ballade des Pendus*, his own epitaph, was written when he was sentenced to be hanged, a sentence later commuted to banishment.

FRANÇOIS-MARIE AROUET de VOLTAIRE (1694–1778), philosopher, historian, and dramatist, was born in Paris. An enemy of organized religion and superstition and a champion of justice, he prepared the way for the French Revolution. His biting wit made him a master of light verse.

Index of Titles

A Monsieur Grétry, 52
A présent laissez-moi, je vais seul, 180
And Now Let Me Be, I Go Alone, 181
Annie, 166
Annie (trans.), 167
Antoine et Cléopatre, 110
Antony and Cleopatra, 111
Art, 81
Avertissement, 142

Ballade, 20
Ballade (extrait de Cyrano de Bergerac), 146
Ballade (from Cyrano de Bergerac), 147
Ballade des dames du temps jadis, 30
Ballade of the Hanged Men, 27
Ballade of the Ladies of Time Past, 31
Ballade—The Hostelry of Thought, 19
Butterfly, The, 59

Carp, 163
Cat, The, 167
Cathay, 145
Chanson d'automne, 120
Child Jesus of Prague, The, 151
Children of the Poor, The, 69
Chinoiserie, 86
Chinoiserie (trans.), 87
Christine à son fils, 16
Christine to Her Son, 17
Colloque sentimentale, 118
Colloque sentimentale (trans.), 119
Colombine, 114
Colombine (trans.), 115
Comme on void sur la branche, 40
Contrerimes, XLIV, 144
Correspondances, 94
Correspondences, 95
Crawfish, 163

Dans la forêt sans heures, 178
De soy mesme, 32
Dieu qu'il la fait, 23
Dog Who Dropped Substance for Shadow, The, 51

Eighth Sonnet, The, 43
El Desdichado, 74
El Desdichado (trans.), 75
Epitaph (Hill, tr.), 77
Epitaph (McElroy, tr.), 129
Epitaph on Himself, 45
Épitaphe (Corbière), 128
Épitaphe (Nerval), 76
Épitaphe de Régnier, 44

Fable, 158
Fable (trans.), 159
Fantaisie, 74
Fantasy, 75
Flawed Bell, The, 103
Flute, The, 55
Foreword, 143

Grasshopper, 163
Grasshopper and the Ant, The, 49

Helen, 155
Hélène, 156
Heureux qui, comme Ulysse, 36
Heureux qui, comme Ulysse (trans.), 37
Hialmar Speaks to the Raven, 91
Hippopotamus, The, 89
Homecoming, 201

I Am No More What Once I Was, 33
Immense and Red, 207
Immense et rouge, 206
Impossible, The, 141
Impromptu on Monsieur Turgot, 53
Impromptu sur M. Turgot, 52
In the Primeval Wood, 179

Invitation to the Voyage, 95
Irene's Pennywhistle, 183

La Carpe, 162
La Cigale et la fourmi, 48
La Cloche fêlée, 102
La Flûte, 54
La Méridienne du lion, 68
La Musique, 98
La Nature, 60
La Pomme de terre, 194
La Sauterelle, 162
Landscape, 101
Larme, 134
Larme (*trans.*), 135
L'Art, 80
Le Chat, 166
Le Chien qui lâche sa proie pour
    l'ombre, 50
Le Ciel est, par-dessus le toit, 116
Le Cœur de Hialmar, 90
Le Crapaud, 126
L'Écrevisse, 162
L'Enfant Jésus de Prague, 150
L'Épitaphe Villon (La Ballade des
    pendus), 26
Le Hareng saur, 106
Le Mirliton d'Irène, 182
Le Naufragé, 110
Le Papillon, 58
Le Piano que baise une main frêle,
    120
Le Pot de fleurs, 86
Le Retour au pays, 200
Le Rossignol, 122
Le Soleil, 198
Le Thé, 104
Le Vierge, le vivace et le bel
    aujourd'hui, 108
Le Vin perdu, 156
Les Enfants pauvres, 68
Les Grenades, 154
Les Roses de Saadi, 56
Les Sapins, 168
Les Sapins (*trans.*), 169

Les Sirènes, 162
L'Hippopotame, 88
Liberté, 186
Liberty, 187
L'Impossible, 140
L'Invitation au voyage, 94
Lion at Noon, The, 69
Little Poem, 161
Lost Sailor, The, 111
Lost Wine, The, 157

Ma Bohème, 134
Marine 132
Marine (*trans.*), 133
Merdrigal, 160
Mountebanks, 171
Muddy Madrigal, 161
Music, 99

Nature, 61
Nightingale, The, 123
Nouveau venu, qui cherches Rome
    en Rome, 34

"O douce Volupté . . . ," 46
Ode to Pleasure, 47

Paysage, 100
Petit Poème, 160
Piano, The, 121
Pomegranates, 155
Pot of Flowers, The, 87
Potato, The, 195
Prayer to Go to Paradise with the
    Donkeys, A, 149
Prière pour aller au Paradis avec
    les ânes, 148
Prise sur le fait, 182

"Quand vous aurez fini de me
    coiffer, j'aurai fini de vous haïr,"
    180
Quand vous serez bien vieille, 38

Rome (*Spenser, tr.*), 35
Rome (*Winters, tr.*), 35
Rondeau (*d'Orléans*), 18, 22

Rondeau (*Villon*), 26
Rondeau (*Wilbur, tr.*), 19
Roses, 41
Roses of Sa'adi, The, 57

Sables mouvants, 200
Sables mouvants (*trans.*), 201
Saison des semailles. Le Soir, 72
Saltimbanques, 170
Scheveningue, morte-saison, 172
Scheveningen, Off Season, 173
Sensation, 130
Sensation (*trans.*), 131
Sigh, 109
Sirens, 163
Sky Is Up Above the Roof, The,
    117
Smoked Herring, The, 107
Soleils couchants, 64
Song of Autumn, 121
Sonnet VIII, 42
Sorrow, 79
Soupir, 108
Sowing at Evening, 73
Stances, *extrait de*, 138

Stances, *from*, 139
Strolling Player, The, 135
Sun, 199
Sunset, A, 65

Tea, 105
Thalassa, 174
Thalassa (*trans.*), 175
To Death, of His Lady, 27
To Monsieur Grétry, 53
Toad, The, 127
Toy qui de Rome, 34
Tristesse, 78

Virelay, 10
Virelay (*trans.*), 11
Virgin, Bright, and Beautiful
    To-day, The, 109
Vowels, 131
Voyelles, 130

When You Are Old, 39
"When You Stop Combing My
    Hair, I'll Stop Hating You," 181

Index of First Lines

A black, E white, I red, U green, O
    blue—I'll tell, 131
A Breton returns to his birthplace,
    201
A following breeze, Arcturus clear
    of clouds, 111
A noir, E blanc, I rouge, U vert, O
    bleu, voyelles, 130
A présent laissez-moi, je vais seul,
    180
A song in a windless night, 127
A tin of corned beef, chained like a
    lorgnette, 159
A triumph in Paris, your songs were
    decried, 53

Across the forest of Delay, 19
Afin que leur fantaisie, 182
All nature is a temple where the
    alive, 95
All things are doubly fair, 81
Am I lovely, am I fair?, 11
And now let me be, I go alone, 181
As one sees on the branch in the
    month of May the rose, 41
Avec la brise en poupe et par un ciel
    serein, 110
Azur! c'est moi...Je viens des
    grottes de la mort, 154

Between Mobile and Galveston, 167

Ce n'est pas vous, non, madame, que j'aime, 86
C'est le moment crépusculaire, 72
C'est un Breton qui revient au pays natal, 200
Chacun se trompe ici-bas, 50
Comme on void sur la branche au mois de May la rose, 40
Comme un vol criard d'oiseaux en émoi, 122
Couché sur le divan au fond de la cabine, 174

Dans la forêt sans heures, 178
Dans la plaine des baladins, 170
Dans le clair petit bar aux meubles bien cirés, 172
Dans le vieux parc solitaire et glacé, 118
Dans mon cœur en ta présence, 160
Dans vos viviers, dans vos étangs, 162
Death, of thee do I make my moan, 27
Demons and wonders, 201
Démons et merveilles, 200
Dieu, qu'il la fait bon regarder, 22
Dites moi où, n'en quel pays, 30
Dures grenades entr'ouvertes, 154

Elle me dit: "Je suis l'impassible théâtre, 60
En la forest de Longue Actente, 18
Everyone is self-deceived, 51

Far from the birds, the herds, the village girls, 135
Fils, je n'ai mie grand trésor, 16
Freres humains qui après nous vivez, 26

God, that mad'st her well regard her, 23
Grasshopper, having sung her song, 49

Great joy be to the sailor if he chart, 37

Here is the delicate grasshopper, 163
Heureux qui, comme Ulysse, a fait un beau voyage, 36

I am always touched by one memory of my youth, 55
I am no more what once I was, 33
I am the stage, impassive, mute and cold, 61
I firmly believe in Turgot, 53
I live, I die. I drown, I am aflame, 43
I love the evenings, passionless and fair, I love the evens, 65
I remember the room I had as a child, 161
I want in my own home, 167
I wanted this morning to bring you a gift of roses, 57
I would more chastely to compose my verse, 101
Ie vis, ie meurs: ie me brule et me noye, 42
Il a vécu, tantôt gai comme un sansonnet, 76
Il est amer et doux, pendant les nuits d'hiver, 102
Il est un air pour qui je donnerais, 74
Il était un grand mur blanc—nu, nu, nu, 106
Il neige. Le grand monde est mort sans doute. C'est décembre, 150
Immense and red, 207
Immense et rouge, 206
In a bright little bar that was carefully waxed, 173
In his lone cave the lion sleeps, 69
In order that their fantasies, 181
In the old park, solitary and vast, 119
In the primeval wood, 179
Incertitude, my secret joy, 163
Incertitude, ô mes délices, 162
It is not you, no, madam, whom I love, 87

It snows, and out of doors perhaps
  the world has died, 151
I've lived my life in careless ease, 45
I've lost my spirit and my strength,
  79

J'ai perdu ma force et ma vie, 78
J'ai, quelque jour, dans l'Océan, 156
J'ai voulu ce matin te rapporter des
  roses, 56
J'aime les soirs sereins et beaux,
  j'aime les soirs, 64
J'ay vécu sans nul pensement, 44
Je crois en Turgot fermement, 52
Je jette avec grâce mon feutre, 146
Je me souviens de ma chambre d'en-
  fant, 160
Je m'en allais, les poings dans mes
  poches crevées, 134
Je puis mourir ce soir! Averses,
  vents, soleil, 140
Je souhaite dans ma maison, 166
Je suis le ténébreux,—le veuf,—l'in-
  consolé, 74
Je veux pour composer chastement
  mes églogues, 100

La cigale, ayant chanté, 48
La cour a dénigré tes chants, 52
La musique souvent me prend
  comme une mer!, 98
La Nature est un temple où de vi-
  vants piliers, 94
La rose du jardin que j'avais mé-
  prisée, 138
Le ciel est, par-dessus le toit, 116
Le lion dort, seul sous sa voûte, 68
Le piano que baise une main frêle,
  120
Le temps a laissié son manteau, 18
Le vierge, le vivace et le bel au-
  jourd'hui, 108
Léandre le sot, 114
Les chars d'argent et de cuivre, 132
Les sanglots longs, 120

Les sapins en bonnets pointus, 168
L'hippopotame au large ventre, 88
Like a clamorous flock of birds in
  alarm, 123
Loin des oiseaux, des troupeaux, des
  villageoises, 134
Lorsqu'il faudra aller vers vous, ô
  mon Dieu, faites, 148

May I not know, Sirens, what stirs
  your discontent, 163
Mélange adultère de tout, 128
Men and brothers, who after us shall
  be, 27
Miss Ellen do, pray, pour the tea, 105
Miss Ellen, versez-moi le Thé, 104
Mon âme vers ton front où rêve, ô
  calme sœur, 108
Mon enfant, ma sœur, 94
Mon père (un dur par timidité), 142
Mongrel bred of every strain, 129
Mort, j'appelle de ta rigueur, 26
My child, my sister, dream, 95
My father, severe because he was
  shy, 143
My hands in pockets worn out at
  the seams, 135
My hat is flung swiftly away, 147
My soul, oh peaceful sister, toward
  your brow where dreams, 109

Naître avec le printemps, mourir
  avec les roses, 58
Night in the bloodstained snow: the
  wind is chill, 91
Nouveau venu, qui cherches Rome
  en Rome, 34
Now is the moment of twilight, 73
Now, like a starling's, all his life was
  gay, 77

O douce Volupté, sans qui, dès notre
  enfance, 46
O Light, 'tis I, who from death's
  other shores, 155

Oh tell me where, in lands or seas, 31
On music drawn away, a sea-borne mariner, 99
On my schoolboy's notebooks, 187
On summer evenings blue, pricked by the wheat, 131
One day into the sea I cast, 157
Oui, l'œuvre sort plus belle, 80

Par les soirs bleus d'été j'irai dans les sentiers, 130
Parfois un enfant trouve une petite graine, 86
Peeling a high-quality boiled potato is an exquisite pleasure, 195
Peler une pomme de terre bouillie de bonne qualité est un plaisir de choix, 194
Pleasure, whom had we lacked from earliest hour, 47
Plunged in wooded pools, 163
Plus ne suis ce que j'ay esté, 32
Pomegranates, fruit whose hard, 155
Prenez garde à ce petit être, 68
Propped on my footstool by the popping log, 103

"Quand vous aurez fini de me coiffer, j'aurai fini de vous haïr," 180
Quand vous serez bien vieille, au soir, à la chandelle, 38

Saché-je d'où provient, Sirènes, votre ennui, 162
Seated on a couch at the rear of my cabin, 175
Soleil en terre, tournesol, 198
Sometimes a small boy finds a tiny seed, 87
Son, of great fortune have I none, 17
Sui je, sui je, sui je belle?, 10
Sun in the earth, sunflower, 199
Sur la côte du Texas, 166
Sur mes cahiers d'écolier, 186

Take heed of this small child of earth, 69
The chariots of silver and copper, 133
The dark one am I, the widowed, unconsoled, 75
The firs have pointed caps to wear, 169
The foolish Leander, 115
The garden rose I paid no honour to, 139
The hippo, huge of abdomen, 89
The lovers pace the terrace nervously, 111
The mountebanks appear like smoke, 171
The piano, kissed by hands not sure nor strong, 121
The sky is up above the roof, 117
The virgin, bright, and beautiful today, 109
The year has cast its cloak away, 19
There is an air for which I'd gladly give, 75
There was a great white wall—bare, bare, bare, 107
Thou stranger, which for *Rome* in *Rome* here seekest, 35
To come to life with spring, and die when dies the rose, 59
Tonight I may die. Rain, wind, sun, 141
Toujours ce souvenir m'attendrit et me touche, 54
Tous deux ils regardaient, de la haute terrasse, 110
Toy qui de Rome emerueillé contemples, 34

Un chant dans une nuit sans air, 126
Une boîte de corned-beef, enchaînée comme une lorgnette, 158
Une nuit claire, un vent glacé. La neige est rouge, 90

Voici la fine sauterelle, 162

Vous qui retournez du Cathai, 144 ·

When a sighing begins, 121

When I must come to you, O my God, I pray, 149

When you are old, at evening candle-lit, 39

"When you stop combing my hair, I'll stop hating you," 181

Within my heart when you are here, 161

You, who behold in wonder Rome and all, 35

You who have from far Cathay, 145

Index of Poets

Apollinaire, Guillaume, 162

Banville, Théodore de, 104
Baudelaire, Charles, 94

Chénier, André, 54
Claudel, Paul, 150
Cocteau, Jean, 182
Corbière, Tristan, 126
Cros, Charles, 106

Desbordes-Valmore, Marceline, 56
Deschamps, Eustache, 10
Desnos, Robert, 198
D'Orléans, Charles, 18
Du Bellay, Joachim, 34

Éluard, Paul, 186

Fargue, Léon-Paul, 160

Gautier, Théophile, 80

Heredia, José Maria de, 110
Hugo, Victor, 64

Jacob, Max, 160
Jammes, Francis, 148
Jarry, Alfred, 158

Labé, Louise, 42
La Fontaine, Jean de, 46

Laforgue, Jules, 140
Lamartine, Alphonse de, 58
Larbaud, Valery, 172
Lisle, Leconte de, 90

Mallarmé, Stéphane, 108
Marot, Clément, 32
Moréas, Jean, 138
Musset, Alfred de, 78

Nerval, Gérard de, 74

Perse, St.-John, 180
Pisan, Christine de, 16
Ponge, Francis, 194
Prévert, Jacques, 200

Régnier, Mathurin, 44
Rimbaud, Arthur, 130
Ronsard, Pierre de, 38
Rostand, Edmond, 146

Supervielle, Jules, 178

Toulet, Paul-Jean, 144

Valéry, Paul, 154
Verlaine, Paul, 114
Vigny, Alfred de, 60
Villon, François, 26
Voltaire, François-Marie Arouet de, 52

Index of Translators

Alexander, Lloyd, 187

Bishop, John Peale, 135
Bithell, Jethro, 131
Bower, Anthony, 75

Cameron, Norman, 131
Chapin, Katherine Garrison, 151
Cornford, Frances, 111
Coulette, Henri, 111
Coxe, Louis O., 169, 201
Creekmore, Hubert, 109

Dowson, Ernest, 117

Ferlinghetti, Lawrence, 201
Fitzgerald, Robert, 27, 99
Flecker, James Elroy, 91, 139
Fraser, G. S., 109

Golffing, Francis, 133

Hecht, Anthony, 37
Hill, Brian, 77, 87
Howes, Barbara, 11, 17, 20, 57, 73,
    75, 79, 89, 105, 157, 179

Jourdain, Margaret, 61

Kennedy, X. J., 163, 199

Lawrence, Merloyd, 195
Legge, J. G., 45, 59
Lloyd, A. L., 107, 159
Lowell, Robert, 103

McElroy, Walter, 129
Marsh, Edward, 121
Martin, Eva, 69
Meredith, William, 167, 171
Moore, Marianne, 51

Plomer, William, 53
Porter, Katherine Anne, 33
Pound, Ezra, 23
Prokosch, Frederic, 43

Reid, Alastair, 183
Rossetti, Dante Gabriel, 27

Santayana, George, 81
Shattuck, Roger, 167
Smith, A. J. M., 87
Smith, William Jay, 135, 141, 143,
    145, 155, 161, 173, 175, 207
Spenser, Edmund, 35
Swinburne, Algernon Charles, 69
Symons, Arthur, 115, 119, 121

Tate, Allen, 95
Taylor, Henry, 55, 101, 123
Thompson, Francis, 65

Untermeyer, Louis, 147

Varèse, Louise, 181

Watkins, Vernon, 41, 127
Wilbur, Richard, 19, 31, 47, 49, 95,
    149
Winters, Yvor, 35
Wolfe, Humbert, 39

ABOUT THE COMPILER

Born in Louisiana, William Jay Smith attended Washington University in St. Louis, where he received his M.A. in French. During World War II he was liaison officer on a French war vessel. After the war he continued his studies at Oxford (as a Rhodes Scholar) and in France and Italy. Mr. Smith is the author of four books of poetry, two of which have been leading contenders for the National Book Award, as well as numerous volumes of poetry for children. He has taught French and English at Washington University and Columbia, and was for several years Poet in Residence at Williams College. He is now Professor of English at Hollins College, Virginia.

ABOUT THE ARTIST

Roger Duvoisin was born in Geneva, Switzerland, and was educated at College Modern, Ecole des Arts et Métièrs, and Ecole des Beaux Arts in Geneva. Mr. Duvoisin has illustrated articles and stories for various American magazines but now devotes full time to writing and illustrating books, mostly juvenile. In 1948, he received the Caldecott Award for his illustrations for *White Snow, Bright Snow*. Mr. Duvoisin's work has been included in many exhibitions, among them the American Graphic Art in Russia and Eastern Europe touring exhibits organized by the State Department. Mr. Duvoisin lives in Gladstone, New Jersey.